CLOCKMAKING

FOR THE
MODEL ENGINEER

by

Colin Thorne LBHI

British Library Cataloguing-in-Publication-Data: a catalogue record of this book is held by the British Library.

This Edition - First Printing 2004
(Originally published, in a different edition, as *Clockmaking for the Home Shop Machinist*
by Guy Lautard, Vancouver, Canada.)

ISBN No. 0-9547131-1-7

Published in Great Britain by:

CAMDEN MINIATURE STEAM SERVICES
Barrow Farm, Rode, Frome, Somerset. BA11 6PS
www.camdenmin.co.uk

Camden stock one of the widest selections of engineering, technical and hot air engine books to be found. Contact them at the above address for a copy of their latest free Booklist.

Layout and design by Camden Studios.

Printed by Cambridge Printing.

IMPORTANT:
Some of the processes and working methods described in this book can potentially be hazardous. The author and publisher are just passing on information – your safety, and that of others, is entirely your responsibility.

TABLE OF CONTENTS

APPENDICES

ILLUSTRATIONS

APPENDIX IV
THE CLOCK DRAWINGS

PHOTOGRAPHS

PREFACE

This little book opens with the words: "There are many model engineers who have a hankering to build a clock... but..." I hope that the following pages can allay the doubt implied by that little word "but".

This book is aimed directly at the experienced model engineer. You will find no instructions on how to get the best from your lathe, how to set up work on the milling machine, or similar sorts of advice. It is assumed that you know these things already, and that you are experienced in the use of hand tools. (The complete novice would be well advised to buy one or more books on basic lathe work and also on general workshop practice.)

Perhaps you have thought you would like to make a clock (a future family heirloom), and would like to know what specialist techniques and tooling are required. This book will take you through the construction of a typical clock, describing, as we come to them, those techniques of the clockmaker that differ from, or are seldom used in, model engineering.

Specialist tools and their uses are also described as the need for them arises during clock construction. Virtually all of these tools can be made by the clockmaker; clockmakers have always been toolmakers as well.

The book is intended as an adjunct to my "Plans for Clockmakers" series of clock and horological tool workshop drawings. Drawings alone are not really enough for the newcomer to clockmaking. I hope this book fills that gap and encourages you to try clockmaking.

Most amateur clockmakers have been encouraged and inspired by the writings of authors such as Claud Reeve, Bill Smith, Alan Timmins and John Wilding, among others. I am no exception, having spent fifteen years designing and making my own clocks as an amateur before turning professional in 1993.

I would also like to acknowledge the help of Guy and Margaret Lautard of Vancouver, Canada; Margaret's typing skills and Guy's editorship ultimately produced the North American edition of the book. The assistance of a professional writer who also appreciates the subject matter cannot be underestimated. My thanks to both.

Colin Thorne

Barnstaple
May 2004

FRONTISPIECE
Clock Movement

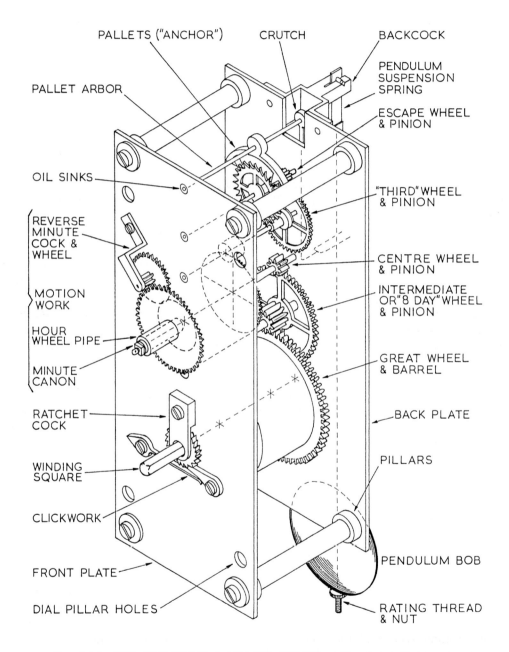

PALLETS ("ANCHOR")

CRUTCH

BACKCOCK

PENDULUM SUSPENSION SPRING

PALLET ARBOR

ESCAPE WHEEL & PINION

OIL SINKS

"THIRD" WHEEL & PINION

REVERSE MINUTE COCK & WHEEL

MOTION WORK

CENTRE WHEEL & PINION

INTERMEDIATE OR "8 DAY" WHEEL & PINION

HOUR WHEEL PIPE

MINUTE CANON

GREAT WHEEL & BARREL

RATCHET COCK

BACK PLATE

WINDING SQUARE

PILLARS

CLICKWORK

FRONT PLATE

PENDULUM BOB

DIAL PILLAR HOLES

RATING THREAD & NUT

A BASIC TIMEPIECE MOVEMENT. Spring driven, pendulum controlled. Recoil ("Anchor") escapement.

Introduction

There are many model engineers who have a hankering to build a clock, but shy away from the task because they think it might be "too fiddly", or need too many specialist tools. While it is true that a few special tools are required, a great outlay is not necessary in either time or money. Some tools, such as clockmakers' broaches or pinion cutters, are best bought, but others - such as a mainspring winder, turns or throw, stakes, milling spindle, flycutting frame, etc. - are really quite quick and easy to make for oneself. Indeed, some tools will *have* to be made, because they can no longer be bought, but the majority can be produced easily in less than a week of evening sessions in the workshop.

As for whether clockmaking is "too fiddly" or not, any model engineer who has constructed Stephenson's or Walschaert's valve gear in 3½" gauge, or a full set of boiler fittings including injectors and tapered plug cocks need have no worries on this score.

It is my hope that this little book will encourage those who would like to make a clock (or several!) to have a go. I shall assume that a lathe and bench drill press are among the tools in your workshop, and that you already know how to get the best from them.

Small lathes such as the UNIMAT or COWELLS are quite suitable for clockmaking, although the increased rigidity of something like a MYFORD is an advantage, especially when milling pinions for example. Screwcutting facilities, while not essential, are certainly very useful. My own lathe is a 60-year old RANDA, 3"centre height, 12" between centres. In spite of its age, it still turns true between centres. It has back gear and screwcutting capabilities. I also have a TOYO precision drill press, but in making my first two clocks, I had nothing more than a BLACK & DECKER "D.I.Y." drill on a stand. This answered my purposes quite well enough, and is still used for drilling holes over 6 mm. diameter.

The usual selection of hand tools is required - but if you have built a locomotive, an internal combustion engine, or a hot air engine, you almost certainly already have a selection of tools suitable for clockmaking.

You will need a lot of files, both larger sizes and needle files. Three or four assorted riffler files will also be very useful. It is best to have two sets, one for steel and one for brass, aluminium etc. Once a file has cut steel it is useless on brass. I have an old 10" file that will cut gauge plate like it was grating cheese, but it just bounces off brass! I have about 60 files, and they all get used regularly.

The only specialist tools you should get before you start are a couple of sets of clockmakers' broaches. These are tapered five-sided cutting broaches, and are used for enlarging holes for fitting pivots in plates, also for forming drive fit holes for fitting wheels to their collets, etc. Use them only for cutting brass. You will need a selection of sizes, from about 0.5mm. up to 10mm. Other specialist tools will be detailed as the need for them arises.

The materials used for clockmaking are mainly brass, silver steel, gauge plate (ground flat stock) and mild steel. The last three mentioned are readily available from the usual model engineering supply houses, but the brass sheet is best obtained from a specialist dealer (see Appendix). Brass rod as supplied by model engineering suppliers is quite satisfactory. It turns cleanly, and is suitable for flycutting small wheels such as ratchets. However, normal "half hard" brass is not suitable for clock plates and wheels - it is simply too "sticky".

The brass required for clockmaking (CZ 120) contains a small amount of lead, which makes it very easy to work and machine. The swarf comes off in small chips and, having turned a leaded brass blank, cutting the teeth in same with a high speed flycutter is pure pleasure. It is variously known as "engraving brass", "compo brass" or simply "clockmakers' brass".

Silver steel rod is used for making pinions and arbors. It is well worth using the freecutting variety (KEA 108), particularly for pinions. It cuts cleanly and takes a polish quickly. It hardens and tempers the same as standard silver steel, and can also be used for making small cutting tools such as flycutters for wheels. Gauge plate - perhaps more commonly known as "ground flat stock" - is used mainly in escapements, but can also be used for cutting tools. Ordinary mild steel or "B.M.S." can be used for all of the steel parts in a clock not specified as needing to be made from silver steel or gauge plate.

The range of lathe tools needed for cutting this modest range of materials is not large, and you probably already have them. A right hand knife tool for turning and facing, plus parting tools, are the basic requirements, but you will need two of each - one for steel and one for brass. Tools for brass must have zero top rake, in fact I find the parting tool cuts better, with less likelihood of chatter, if it has negative top rake: 3° or 4° seems to suit my lathe. The same tools for cutting steel need about 12° to 15° of top rake. I find that the parting tool works better with slightly more. My favourite parting tool for steel has about 20° top rake.

I have a special toolbit for cutting small arbors of φ2mm. or less. It looks very much like a thread cutting tool with an included angle of about 50° and about 30° to top rake coming straight back from the tip, the latter having a minute radius stoned on it. With a workpiece up to 35 or 40 mm. long and of such a small diameter, you must obviously take very light cuts at fine feed; this tool seems to do the job well. The finish is not great because such a small part of the cutting edge is in contact with the work, but these pieces will be finished with a hand graver in any case, so this is not a problem. Using the hand graver is covered in the chapter on arbors and pivots.

A couple of round nosed tools for brass will also prove useful when cutting decorative pillars, etc. One with a tip radius of about 0.5mm. and another of about 1.5mm. will be fine. The straight sides coming back from the tip should have an included angle of about 45°, to enable the cutting tip to get into both left and right hand corners. Boring tools are not required very often, but keep a couple handy - a small one, and a very small one!

High speed steel (HSS) is my preferred material for lathe tools. HSS drills, lathe tool bits, and blanks are readily available from model engineers' suppliers, as well as local industrial supply houses. For cutting brass, tools can be quickly and easily made from silver steel or gauge plate. Rough out to shape with files; harden and temper to straw; and bring to finished shape on a grinder if necessary, before finishing with slip stones. I can file pretty close to

finished size, but a touch on the grinder gives nice flat surfaces, even concave if required, and sharp, straight edges. As you have to polish between hardening and tempering, in order to see the colour, it is easy to spoil a nice sharp edge, so I always leave a "whisker" to be removed on the grinder, particularly with form tools, e.g. flycutters for producing wheel teeth.

There are no specific screw threads used in clock-making. I favour the BA series, and use and specify the even numbers from 0 BA to 10 BA inclusive, but the nearest metric, BSF, or North American size is equally suitable. Steel cheese head screws are the most common type used in clockmaking, but where countersunk screws are specified, the screw is often of the same material as the piece it is securing, which is, more often than not, brass.

You can make all your own screws, but this is doing things the hard way. I keep a small stock of steel cheese head screws in 10, 8, 6 and 4 BA sizes and brass countersunk in 10, 8 and 6 BA. Keep long ones in stock, and shorten them as required. I have a few assorted 2 and 0 BA screws in stock, but I more often make these when required, which is rarely. If I require a steel countersunk screw, I turn down the head of a cheese head screw. They are easy to hold in the little tool shown in Fig. 4; lock them in with a nut.

Shouldered screws such as are used for click pivots will have to be made. I cut the thread with a die in the tailstock, turning the die "back to front" for a second cut right up to the shoulder. Lightly counter-sink the mouth of the tapped hole in the plate to ensure that the screw sits tight down on its shoulder.

Although they are not needed very often, it is handy to keep a few nuts in stock. When a nut is required, it is usually an odd one like a square or a large hex, and has to be made for the job in any case.

So much for the preliminaries. I will now detail the parts of a clock in the order in which they would be made, and how methods might differ from normal model engineering practice.

Plates

The plates of a clock are equivalent to the frames of a locomotive or the hornplates of a traction engine. They are joined together by pillars (in a loco-motive, the equivalent items are called frame stretchers). Plates and pillars together form a rigid box structure which is the "chassis" of the clock.

On a bracket or longcase clock the plates are simply rectangular plates of brass. On a skeleton clock they are referred to as frames, and many elegant designs have been used.

Plain rectangular plates are easily cut out with a hacksaw. If you are ordering your brass sheet cut to size, specify it about 5mm. oversize in both dimensions. When it comes to hand, you may find that it was cut on a guillotine which has left a rounded edge on one face. This does not look well on a clock plate, hence enough surplus material is needed to allow for the removal of this offending area.

Skeleton clock frames are a different matter. Some cuts can be made with a hacksaw, but you will soon work your way into a corner. They can be cut out by chain drilling, but this becomes tedious. The best tool is the "Abrafile" or tension file, which can be purchased with adaptor clips to fit into a hacksaw frame. It will cut in any direction - corners, curves, etc. are no problem. Tension it in the hacksaw frame the same as you would a normal blade. Unless it is really taut it will flex and break. If you will but let it cut at its own speed, you can easily cut out a pair of frames with one blade and no breakages. And don't throw away the broken blades - they will fit your piercing saw frame; for more on this topic, see the chapter on wheel cutting and crossing out. In making a set of clock plates, the first requirement is that the plates can be readily placed together at will,in perfect register, for drilling holes common to both, and can be realigned easily and accurately whenever the need arises. This is done using "steady pins" (which an engineer would call "register pins"), which are fixed to one plate, and which locate in a corresponding hole in the other. Register pins are made from standard clock pins. These are tapered steel or brass pins, and come in a range of gauged sizes. They are not stepped in an entirely logical progression, and some have more taper than others; all are referred to by their particular gauge numbers. The "universal" pin is 25mm. long and tapers from 1.8mm. to 0.7mm. This is the one to use for steady pins.

Steady pins should be made of the same material as the item of which they are to become a part: brass

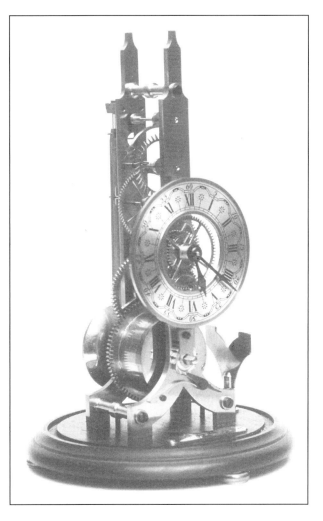

A small and simple 8 day skeleton timepiece.

plate = brass pins. It is quite easy to make tapered pins by holding a piece of wire in a pin chuck and resting it on a wood bed. Rotate the chuck stem between thumb and forefinger while running a file over the wire. They are cheap enough to buy, however, and you will need quite a few, so you may wish to buy a stock of them.

To fit steady pins, clamp the two roughly cut plates together and drill a hole of about 1.2mm. diameter near each of the top and bottom edges. Before drilling, make sure that the position of these holes will not interfere with any future fittings, pillars, backcock, pivot holes etc. From the front face of what will be the front plate, run in a clockmaker's broach until each hole is tapered right through. On the back face of the front plate, countersink the hole slightly, to prevent a burr being raised, and tap a clock pin in from the front. Cut off all but 1mm. of the upstanding pin, file off the burr, and then hammer it in flush by resting the plate on a clock maker's stake, with the pin sunk in a hole in the stake (see Fig. 2). File the area smooth, using first a

Fig I. <u>de-burring tool for clock pins etc.</u>

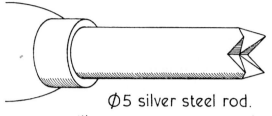

Ø5 silver steel rod.
file two vees across end.
harden and temper. fit to file handle.

riffler file and then successively finer grades of emery wrapped around a block of balsa wood or cork. Finish off with Water of Ayre stone moistened with saliva.

When the above work is done adequately, you should not be able to see where the pin is from the front side of the plate, particularly after you have polished the plate prior to final assembly of the finished clock.

The holes in the back plate will now need easing with a taper broach until the two plates sit together flush. On both sides of the back plate, take off any burrs by lightly countersinking the holes. The plates can then be placed together and separated any number of times for filing, drilling etc. Leave the pins in the finished clock - they may be needed in the future during repair work. Fit the plates together and cut off the excess length of pin flush with the surface of the back plate, and take off the burr. A simply made de-burring tool is shown in Fig. 1.

"What is a clockmaker's stake?" you may ask. You possibly already have one - engineers call it a bench block or bench stake. Fig. 2 shows a typical small bench stake and a vice stake; their use is obvious. If made from mild steel and not casehardened, they are easily re-faced if damaged, and there is less risk of breaking a hardened clock part. A couple of sizes of each type will be found useful.

The plates can now be clamped together in the vice for filing to shape. Use thick cardboard between the vice jaws and the work. If any swarf falls between the plates and the cardboard, it will become embedded in the cardboard, hence will not scratch the plates. File the plates to the scribed outline, but remember that on a clock, particularly a skeleton clock, the remains of the scribed lines must not be seen on the finished job. You cannot use the engineer's dodge of a row of centre punch marks along the line!

The finished edges of the plates must be square and the corners sharp, although one should run a very fine file along the sharp edges to remove burrs. Finish the edges by draw filing, followed by successively finer grades of emery sticks. The plates, including these edges, will eventually be polished, but not until the clock is completed and being assembled for the last time.

Probably the only holes which can be drilled at this stage are the ones for the pillars. There are usually four, one near each corner. Some clocks use five or six pillars, and skeleton clocks may have more than that. One or maybe two of the pivot holes can be drilled at this stage, but most of these will be accurately "planted" using a depthing tool, when the wheels and pinions are finished, of which more anon.

If any pivot holes can be located now (probably only the centre hole and maybe the barrel arbor holes) drill them well undersize for now, just to locate their position; they can be opened out to the correct size once we've made the arbors to match them to.

All other holes are best left until the item they relate to is ready for fitting. Some holes go through both plates, while others go through only one plate, hence the need for steady pins to "register" the plates at any time in the future.

Any scribing done on the plates must be done very lightly, and as locally as possible. Marking out blue can be used, but I prefer "magic marker" broad felt pens. These are easy to apply, and easily removed with the usual solvents. Apart from the outline of the plates, any scribing should do no more than scratch through the blueing. Scribed lines will usually be used for marking hole locations, which should be punched immediately to avoid losing their positions.

Fig 2. <u>typical bench and vice stakes.</u>

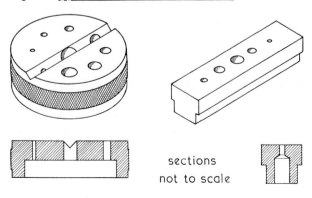

sections
not to scale

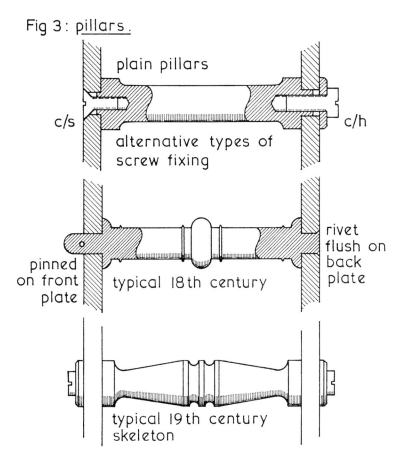

Fig 3 : pillars.

plain pillars

c/s   alternative types of   c/h
             screw fixing

pinned   typical 18th century   rivet
on front   flush on
plate   back
                                               plate

typical 19th century
skeleton

Pillars

Pillars are the next item required in order to join the plates together to form the "chassis"of the clock. They are turned from brass rod. Fig. 3 shows several types of pillar, as well as the most common ways of securing them. Modern clock pillars are usually secured by screws.

The hole in the plate is about 1½ to 2 times the diameter of the screw, and a spigot is turned on the end of the pillar to fit this hole. (You won't find this on the average alarm clock; we're talking about quality work!) A fairly good fit is required, but a small chamfer on the end of the spigot is useful to facilitate fitting, particularly of the second plate. For the same reason, a slight countersink is put on the hole. The screw is usually a steel cheese head, finely polished, and is used in conjunction with a brass washer of the same diameter as the pillar. The washer should have a chamfer machined on its outer edge, and the screw should be blued by heating and quenching in oil. This blueing, traditional on high class work, is done purely for appearance, not to harden the steel.

Cheese head screws as supplied are usually too coarsely finished for clock work. Make yourself a

little threaded mandrel for holding in the 3-jaw as shown in Fig. 4. Give this item a punch centre mark for the No. 1 jaw postion, for accurate future re-chucking. Make one for each thread size as you require it, and keep them all for future use. With the screw in the mandrel, take a skim off the circumference, and also across the face to leave a nice sharp edge. Finally, give the screw head a nice polish with emery sticks.

Sometimes it is necessary to keep the plate clear of projections in the vicinity of the pillars (to clear strike work, etc.); in this case a countersunk screw can be used. In this particular case, the previously mentioned rule of countersunk screws being of the same material as that which they are securing is broken, as these screws look much nicer if they are also made of blued steel. The screw may need to be of a smaller size than the cheese head variety, and the spigot on the end of the pillar will also have to protrude less in order that the screw can be driven home fully. This is illustrated in Fig. 3, at top left.

The end faces of the pillars should be made slightly concave, to ensure that the pillar sits tight and square on the plate - see Fig. 5. A few "thou" is all that is required, and this obviously applies to whatever method is used to secure the pillars. The washers should also be made concave on their underside, for the same reason.

The other common method of securing pillars is by pinning, or pinning one end and riveting the other.

Fig 4. threaded mandrel for cleaning/polishing screw heads.

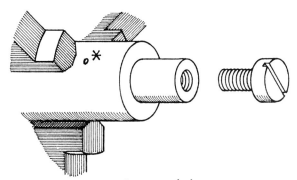

*: centre pop for no.1 jaw.

This is the classic method used on longcase clocks, and is illustrated in Fig. 3. The cross hole for the pin should "underlap" the plate by about a quarter of its diameter so that the tapered clock pin, when driven in, pulls the pillar tight up to the plate. This may seem a little crude, but it is a very effective and secure way of holding the plate. The general rule with clock pins used in this manner is: "brass parts - steel pin" and vice versa.

The method is not much used on skeleton clocks for frame pillars, but it is used for dial pillars. On long-case clocks the other end of the pillar is riveted into the back plate. Drill the hole in the plate slightly undersize, and then open it out with a clockmaker's broach until the spigot on the pillar is a light drive fit. Open the hole from the pillar side of the plate until the spigot will go in about half way. A slight countersink is put on the hole on the outside of the plate. The pillar is driven home and the spigot, which obviously must project slightly, is hammered into the countersink. The surface is then made flush with file, emery and Water of Ayre stone in the same way as described for steady pins. Again, you should not be able to see where the rivet is when the job is finished.

When fitting pillars this way, make sure that the cross hole for the clock pin is at right angles to the nearest edge of the plate; otherwise you may find it difficult to insert the pin when assembling the clock, or - worse - impossible to remove the pin later. This must be borne in mind whenever clock pins are used to secure any component.

Although riveting pillars to the back plate is traditional practice, I must admit to having a distaste for it myself. When making a clock, one cannot have

Fig 5. section through end of pillar showing concavity.

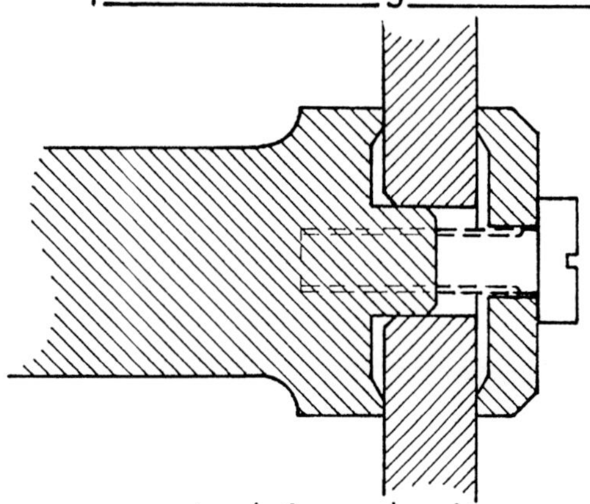

exaggerated for clarity.

a trial assembly until all the wheel work is completed, because once riveted, the pillars are fixed in position, the plates cannot be placed together for drilling pivot holes etc. This problem can be got around by using what the old clockmakers called an "uprighting tool", a clockmaker's tool for ensuring that holes drilled in one plate are properly lined up with the corresponding holes in the other plate.

A modern drill press will serve the same purpose. However, riveting of the pillars is pretty permanent, which makes it difficult to clean and polish the plates in the course of making the clock, not to mention being likely to hinder future repair work. Thus, when I am building a "reproduction" clock, where the pillars would have been riveted to the backplate in the original, while it may not be "correct", I prefer to use countersunk screws to secure them, and use the traditional clock pins on the front plate. There are ways of temporarily holding or pinning the pillars until you are ready to rivet them permanently, but I consider it a distinct advantage to be able to remove them easily at any time in the future.

Having said all that, I will state that I do rivet dial pillars to the back of my dial plates, but the possible future need for complete disassembly does not normally arise here.

One final word on clock pins. Once fitted, they should be cut to a length equal to about three times the diameter of the spigot or post they are fitted through, with equal lengths projecting each side, to look neat and tidy. Finally, remove the pin, file the ends square across, de-burr, and then reinsert it.

A word or two on turning the more ornamental pillar profiles in Fig. 3 may be worth adding. The skeleton clock pillar is fairly straightforward, the tapers being turned by whatever method you would normally use, e.g. by angling the topside. Another quick method which avoids altering the settings on your lathe is to turn the part between centres, using an offset tailstock centre. This is quite suitable for decorative or non-critical tapers. The grooves can be formed by plunge cutting with a round nosed tool before turning the tapers.

The 18th century pillar is another matter. An engineer might suggest using form tools, but they are a bit brutal for this job, and are almost certain to leave chatter marks, which will require more work and time to remove. There is also the fact that form tools take time to make. The quickest way is to form the pillars to a "square" profile by plunge cutting with a broad parting tool, and then form the curves by hand with a graver. If you have never tried this before, you will be surprised at just how quickly you can convert solid metal to swarf! Two gravers are shown in Fig. 6.

Make one from 3 mm. square silver steel (if you can get the stuff), otherwise cut a strip from the edge of a piece of gauge plate. A slightly larger one 4 mm. square would also be useful. While you are at it, make a round one from 5 mm. round bar - this one will be useful for concave surfaces. Make them about 130 mm. long, and fit each one to a small file handle (a round wooden one, not those horrible flat plastic things). Harden the working end, but do not temper - leave it glass hard. Old square and rat tail files also make very good gravers. Grind off the teeth, break off the pointed end, and then grind the cutting face angle. Use a fine Arkansas stone to remove any burrs on the cutting edges.

There is no mystery to hand turning with a graver. If your lathe hasn't got a hand turning tool rest, just clamp a length of 8 or 10 mm. steel bar in the tool-post and set this bar parallel with the job. It should be about 8 to 10 mm. below centre height, and about the same distance from the work. You can present to the work whichever cutting edge of the graver you feel comfortable with, but remember you are cutting brass, so give plenty of negative top rake, either by

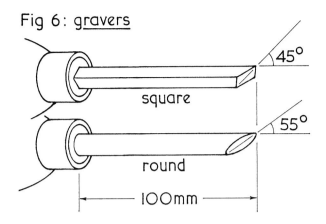

Fig 6: gravers

square 45°

round 55°

100mm

lifting the handle, by twisting the tool so that the cutting edge you are using is at an angle to the axis of the work, or a combination of both. If you do not do so, there is the chance of a dig in. This can be painful, and you may find the graver embedded either in the ceiling or in some part of your anatomy! Run the lathe at about 500 rpm. Practise first by rounding off the corners of a piece of faced scrap brass bar held in the 3-jaw. You will find that with practice you can cut and shape brass without using a tool rest, although this does depend a little on what shape you are trying to achieve. We will come to turning silver steel with a graver later on; that requires a different technique, and is a much more serious matter!

Barrels and Clickwork

The barrel is the clock's power source, and is usually quite a substantial item, whether it is driven by a spring or a weight. Fig. 7 shows these two main types.

Dealing with the spring driven barrel first, the barrel assembly is free to rotate on the barrel arbor, which in turn is free to rotate between the plates. There is a hook on the arbor to secure the inner end of the spring, and a similar hook on the inside face of the barrel for the outer end of the spring. When the arbor is wound with the key, the spring obviously tightens around it, and tries to pull the barrel and attached great wheel after it. At the other end of the wheel train, the clock's escapement allows the

release of the spring's stored energy to occur in a controlled and regulated manner.

It will be seen that the spring will pull the great wheel in the same direction as that in which it is wound, therefore the clock does not stop when you wind it. This action is known as maintaining power, and in this case is automatic, needing no extra parts to provide it. This system is known as a going barrel.

The clickwork, which prevents the spring from unwinding itself, and which enables you to wind it up, is usually on the outside of the front plate. There is a ratchet wheel which fits on the winding square, and a mating pawl, which a clockmaker refers to as a click. A leaf spring bears on the click to keep it in engagement with the ratchet, while a cock covers the ratchet to keep it in position against the plate - see Fig. 13.

The weight driven barrel, on the other hand, is fixed to its arbor, and the ratchet wheel is actually one of the barrel end covers. The great wheel is free to rotate on the arbor next to the ratchet, and the click and click spring are fixed to the face of the rim of the great wheel. The great wheel is retained on the arbor by a slip washer in a groove on the arbor. On weight driven clocks the great wheel usually drives the centre wheel directly, with no intermediate wheel, therefore it revolves anti-clockwise. The barrel, when driving, must revolve in the same direction, so it is wound clockwise.

You are probably ahead of me now, and have realised that during the act of winding, all power is removed from the train, such that the escape wheel may stop, or even run backwards. This momentarily affects the timekeeping of the clock, and this, although of little consequence in a domestic clock, is quite undesirable in a regulator, or other types of clock built for high accuracy performance. There is also a small chance that the pallets can catch the tips of the escape wheel teeth, and bend or even break them. This chance is very small, however, and there are thousands of longcase clocks that have survived centuries without this happening, but it is the reason longcase pendulums have such long suspension springs - they put a bit of resilience into the system. I will deal with maintaining power later, but first let us consider the construction of spring and weight barrels.

Dealing with spring barrels first, the obvious item to start with is the arbor. Make the arbor from silver steel. The thick diameter is usually a stock size, and therefore needs no turning. If your 3-jaw does not

Fig 7 : barrels & clickwork.

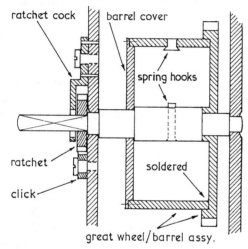

spring barrel.

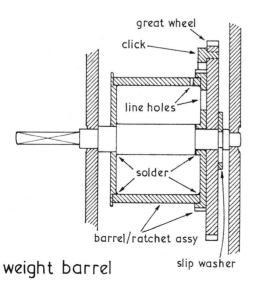

weight barrel

run true, use the 4-jaw or a collet. Turn one end, reverse in the chuck, and turn the other end.

We should pause here to identify two important things that must be borne in mind when turning arbors of any size for any position in the clock: endshake and pivot diameter. The arbor must be perfectly free between the plates and must therefore have a small amount of "endshake". For most clocks, 0.2 or 0.3 mm. is about right, so if the pillars are 50 mm. long, the arbors will be 49.8 mm. - or thereabouts - between the shoulders. This is the sort of thing that is really best checked on the job.

When the arbor is reversed in the chuck for turning, measuring this dimension calls for a little gauge as shown in Fig. 8. This item can be made from any suitable material about 1 to 1.5 mm. thick. Ensure that the indicated measurement is exactly the same as that between the clock plates. Arbor length between shoulders is then easily checked when you are turning the second end. The thin end of the gauge will fit between the chuck jaws to reach, and measure from, the hidden shoulder. Turn the second pivot shoulder back to give the required endshake in the gauge.

With a spring barrel there is a second endshake to consider, and that is the endshake of the arbor within the barrel. In this case, it is easier to turn the centre part of the arbor to nominal length, and then provide the endshake when making the barrel. A good general rule in "one off" clock work, where two items have only to fit each other, is to make the first item to nominal size, and make the second item to fit.

The exact diameter of the pivot is not too important, because we follow the above rule and make each pivot hole in the plates to fit its particular pivot. Obviously the pivot should be turned as close to nominal size as possible, but far more important is the final finish; it must be burnished to a mirror finish.

This is done using pivot files and a burnisher. The latter can be made as required, but pivot files will have to be purchased, They are extremely fine and hard files, similar to a pillar needle file, but with two safe edges. They also come left- and right-handed, in that the safe edges are not at right angles to the cutting face but inclined back about 10°. This is so that they will cut right into the corner between pivot and shoulder. Engineers do not like a sharp angle here because of the increased risk of stress fractures, but clockmakers have been doing it this way for

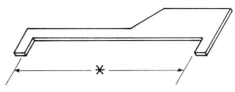

Fig 8 : gauge for measuring for endshake when turning arbors .

✳ : equal to distance between clock plates .

centuries with no problem. There is a good reason for it, which we will come to later.

The pivot file is used with the work revolving in the lathe. A single-roller filing rest is useful to ensure that the pivot remains parallel. After the pivot file, use emery sticks of ever finer grades, finishing with 1200 grit, after which the pivot must be burnished.

The burnisher is basically a file with no teeth! Burnishers are made from silver steel or gauge plate, and are hardened but not tempered. The simplest type is a piece of 5 mm. square about 150 mm. long with one end set into a file handle. One very useful form of burnisher is oval in section and comes to a fine point. Fig. 9 shows a selection of burnisher sections. The burnisher is rubbed over the work while it is revolving in the lathe, in the same way as the pivot file, but at a slightly lower speed and with more pressure, and will quickly bring up a mirror-like finish. When using a burnisher, lubricate with a heavy oil such as motor car engine oil, to avoid "picking up". The burnisher should be rubbed on very fine emery paper every so often to "dress" it. Dress it at right angles to the direction it will be used on the work.

You should now have pivots and bearing surfaces in which you can see your face! On a large arbor such

Fig 9 : pivot burnishers

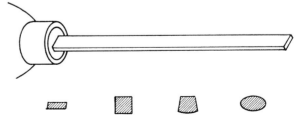

typical cross sections . the oval one tapers to a point .
carbon steel , hardened , not tempered .

Fig 10 : <u>barrel arbor spring hook.</u>

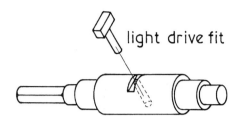

Fig IOA

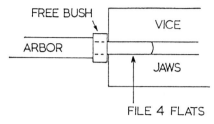

FILING WINDING SQUARES

as a barrel arbor, all the above work can be performed on the lathe, holding the arbor in the 3-jaw chuck or a collet. Smaller and more delicate pivots demand a different technique, which we will describe later, along with proper procedures for fitting them to the pivot holes in the plates.

The barrel arbor requires a spring hook to anchor the inner end of the spring. One easy way is to screw in, and "Loctite" in place, a steel countersunk screw, leaving the head proud. A neater and much more satisfactory method is shown in Fig. 10. When filing the hook to shape, bear in mind the direction in which the spring is to be wound.

The winding square can be milled using the vertical slide on the lathe, or on a milling machine if you have one. It can also be filed by hand in the 3-jaw by using a double roller filing rest. If it is milled, you will have to file and emery it to remove the machining marks. It should be finished to a very fine emery polish. I prefer to file winding squares by hand and eye in the bench vice - in the time it takes to set up the work in the milling machine, I will have the square rough filed and ready for finishing. First turn up a little brass bush, making it a free running fit over the pivot area, to protect it and also to form a stop for the file to ensure that all four sides of the square are the same length. Fit the bush over the pivot and grip the arbor horizontally in the vice by the end you are going to file square. See Fig. 10A.

Counting your strokes, file the first flat until you think you have gone not quite far enough. It is easy to see if you are filing parallel to the centre line because if you are not, the flat formed will be narrower towards the "high" end. Turn the piece through 90° so that the flat is against one of the jaws, and file the second flat the same number of strokes. Likewise for flats 3 and 4. The square can now be measured with a vernier caliper or similar, and a few strokes taken off each flat in turn until the required across flats measurement is reached. It can then be finished with emery sticks, and the sharp edges taken off the square.

The end of the squared arbor should be domed and polished. This can be done by hand in the lathe, using files and emery sticks.

It is probably best to make the barrel before the great wheel and barrel cover. That way, when turning the latter parts to fit the barrel, the finished barrel can be offered up to them to check for size as they are being machined.

The barrel is simply a short piece of brass tube faced square and machined to length. The outside diameter may need a fine clean-up cut, but usually emery paper will give a good finish without any further work. Check that the tube stock you're working with is truly circular. The barrel hook for the spring must be fitted, and in this case a counter-sunk screw is satisfactory; refer again to Fig. 7. A proper stud can be turned and riveted in place, but a screw is more secure in the long run. Screw it in from the inside, cut off slightly proud on the outside and rivet it well down into the threads. Finally, file and polish smooth. When finished, the barrel hook should be invisible on the outside

The next item is the great wheel. The best way to turn and cut wheels is by mounting them on a Morse taper arbor mounted in the lathe. A typical arbor is shown in Fig. 11. The Morse taper can be made from a soft lathe centre, and a selection of screw-in arbors can be made for different sizes of wheel centre holes.

Wheel blanks can be bought, but it is cheaper to cut them from a large sheet of compo brass. Mark the

Fig 11 : <u>lathe mandrel & arbors</u>
<u>for wheelcutting.</u>

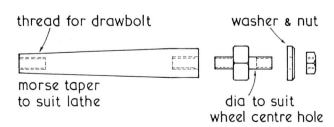

diameter a little over size and drill/ream the centre hole. Saw the blank out square and then cut off the corners to make an octagon. The blank is then mounted on the arbor for turning the outside diameter. The great wheel usually has a recess for fitting the barrel. The barrel should be a light push fit in its recess, and is later soft soldered in position, once the wheel is finished and the teeth have been cut. At this stage the centre hole in the wheel should be smaller than the final diameter required to fit the pivot.

The teeth have now to be cut. We will consider teeth profiles etc. in the chapter on wheels and pinions, but I will deal here with the methods of cutting them.

If you have a milling machine, and a dividing head with the same Morse taper as your lathe, then the job is easy. Likewise, if you have a dividing attachment to fit the outboard end of your headstock spindle, dividing in the lathe is no problem.

My own preference is for direct division from a dividing plate mounted on the rear of the lathe mandrel, as this approach is quick, easy and positive. There have been many methods of dividing in the lathe described in the model engineering press over the years, so I will not digress into a description of them all here. Fig. 28, in the chapter on wheel cutting, shows the direct division method.

If you intend to use a milling machine, you will probably need to use multi-tooth form-relieved cutters to cut your clock wheel teeth, because it is unlikely the machine will be capable of the 5/6,000 rpm required by a single point flycutter. These multi-tooth form-relieved cutters are available for clock wheel teeth profiles, but are very expensive. Of course, one can make one's own such cutters. This process has also appeared in the model engineering press at fairly regular intervals.

However, the quickest way to cut teeth in brass wheels is with a single point high speed flycutter.

The flycutting spindle is mounted on the vertical slide, to provide the downfeed necessary for the control of tooth depth. To actually cut the teeth, the saddle is moved a short distance to and fro along the lathe bed for each tooth; the lathe spindle is then indexed by whatever method you are using, and the next tooth cut.

A simple flycutting attachment is shown in Fig. 12. Plain cone bearings are quite satisfactory, as the stresses involved are very small. The spindle is silver

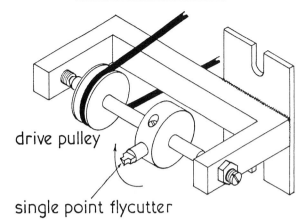

Fig 12 : flycutting frame for use on lathe vertical slide.

drive pulley

single point flycutter

steel with its conical ends hardened, tempered, and polished. The bearings can be brass or bronze. Make sure there is neither axial nor radial play in the spindle before you start to use the attachment.

The spindle needs an external power source to drive it; a small motor of about 80 watts is ample. Pulley sizes should be selected to give an arbor speed of 5000 or 6000 rpm. My current flycutting attachment has a sewing machine motor attached to it, thus making it self-contained. The first one I made, some 20 years ago, was driven via a long stretchy belt from the drill press.

You may already have a milling spindle and drive set-up for use on your lathe, and will therefore need only to make a little carrier for the flycutter bits to fit your spindle. Making these bits will be covered later, when we come to teeth profiles in the chapter on wheels and pinions.

The barrel cover can now be turned on the same arbor that held the great wheel blank for turning. The step should be a very light push fit into the barrel, and the outside diameter exactly the same as that of the barrel. The traditional way of fitting barrel covers is a firm "clip-in" push fit, a recess for this being turned in the barrel end. However, levering them off at some future date inevitably leaves a scar on both barrel and cover. This does not look nice, particularly on fine skeleton clocks, and for this reason I prefer the recess on a fairly thick (2.5 or 3 mm.) cover to push into the barrel for locational purposes only, the cover then being secured by three 10 BA or 12 BA c/s brass screws through the cover flange into the barrel end. This does necessitate a fairly thick barrel also, 2.5 to 3 mm., but gives the advantage of providing a more secure fixing for the spring hook. Also, a thick barrel doesn't get distorted if the spring breaks!

Fig 13 : <u>clickwork detail</u>.

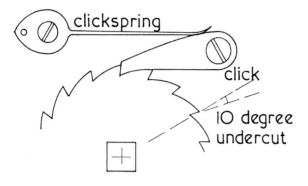

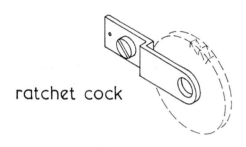

That finishes the barrel assembly. Next comes the clickwork. This is a simple ratchet and pawl assembly, the pawl being referred to as a "click" as noted earlier.

The ratchet is another job of wheel turning and tooth cutting. The profile of the ratchet teeth is not too critical as long as they are made deep enough to amply resist the force of the spring. Equally important is that the shape of the ratchet teeth be such that the click cannot jump out of engagement. To ensure this, the acting faces of the teeth are given about a 10° undercut, or 'draw', as shown in Fig. 13. They also look more attractive if the outer, or non-working face is slightly convex, as shown, although this is purely aesthetic - it will work just as well if made straight.

Another point of importance is that the tips of the teeth are sharp, with no radius whatsoever. This is to ensure that the click cannot catch on the tooth tip, only to fly off and strip all the teeth when the key is released during winding! The click must fall cleanly from one inclined face to the next, and when at rest, the end of the click must fit the tooth space exactly. The ratchet is normally made of brass, and the click of mild steel, or gauge plate. The click does not need hardening, so mild steel is adequate, and slightly easier to work. The hole in the centre of the ratchet is filed square to a free but close fit over the winding square. It may need a small counterbore in the back

face to ensure it clears the pivot diameter and sits flat against the clock plate.

The click is retained by a shouldered screw which screws into the clock plate; the click pivots on the shoulder. This screw is best made from silver steel, although it does not need hardening. If it is a stiff fit in the female thread in the plate, so much the better, as the consequence of this screw working loose can be catastrophic! The female thread can be cut with a taper tap taken in to slightly less than the full thread diameter of the tap, or just far enough for the screw to be run in half way with your fingers. The click should be perfectly free, with minimal end play when the screw is fully driven home.

The click spring is often made of brass, but can also be mild steel, or hardened and tempered gauge plate. It is retained by a single screw, plus one or two steady pins. If made of brass or mild steel, the spring portion can be work hardened by hammering it. It must bear on the click fairly close to the pivot screw, so that a very small movement from the spring ensures a quick return action to the tip of the click when the clock is wound.

Theoretically, the ideal layout is for the ratchet wheel centre, the active ratchet tooth and the click centre pivot to form a right angle. In practice this will lead to a click of ungainly shape. Increasing the angle to 110° or 120° allows a more elegantly shaped click, and ensures a more positive locking action as well.

Although not shown on the drawing, clicks often have an elegantly shaped "tail". This is partly aesthetic, but it also makes it easier to release the click when letting the mainspring down before doing any work on the clock.

The proper procedure for letting down the mainspring of a clock is as follows: the torque of the spring is taken up with the key, after which the click tail is pushed in to disengage the click from the ratchet, and the spring is carefully let down about half a turn at a time with the key, the click being re-engaged between each half turn. You must be very careful when doing this. A slipping click or key can easily strip both the ratchet teeth and your knuckles! If the click was not provided with a tail by its maker, you can ease it out of engagement with a small screwdriver, or something similar, for each half turn.

The ratchet wheel is usually retained in position on the winding square by means of a "cock", also shown in Fig. 13. This is normally made of brass, again retained with a single screw and a steady pin or two. It should allow a tiny amount of end play to the ratchet so that there is no tendency for it to score the clock plate when winding.

An engineer would probably want so set the cock up on the lathe's vertical slide, or in the milling machine vice, and you can do it that way if you wish, but it will still have to be finished by hand to remove machining marks. It really takes very little time to rough it out with a hacksaw and finish it with files.

It is easier to drill the holes (except for the steady pins) before roughing it to shape; the holes then become datum points for filing to finished outline. An easy way to file a neat semicircular end is to turn up a little mild steel button with two diameters. The small diameter fits the hole in the job, which is then filed down to the button's larger diameter. There will be several occasions when these buttons are useful in making a clock, so keep them all for future use.

The easiest way to ensure nice flat surfaces when filing small parts such as these is to clamp the file in the vice, and rub the workpiece along it - much more control can be exercised in this way. Fig. 14 explains. Use a file that is dead straight and with a safe edge.

The ratchet wheel cock is finished and polished with fine files and emery sticks. The best way to do this without any tendency to round off flat surfaces and sharp corners is to rest the work on a resilient surface - possibly the fingers of one hand; the face being treated will then want to stay flat against the

emery stick, etc. I find resting the work on the palm of my hand and letting it "float" with the emery stick is the best way.

Although it is not the case with the ratchet cock, the positioning of some cocks - the reverse minute cock for example - can be quite critical. Whether critical or not, the same procedure is followed. The cock is positioned by eye, and the location of the holding screw in the plate can be spotted through the already-drilled cock. The hole in the plate is then drilled and tapped. (In some cases the tapped hole may be in the cock.) The clearance hole can be opened out slightly if required for freedom of positioning, and the cock is then held lightly with the screw, its exact position determined, and the screw tightened.

The holes for the steady pins are then drilled through both cock and plate, and the steady pins fitted to the cock as already described in the section dealing with the plates. Some cocks only require one steady pin, the ratchet cock probably being such a case, but for exact, repeatable location, two steady pins are necessary.

We now come to weight driven barrels. The main difference between this type and a spring driven barrel is that in the former the barrel assembly is fixed to the arbor. Traditionally this was done by force fit or soft solder. The latter method is the easier to do, although today "Araldite" or "Loctite" are equally suitable. However, my own preference is for soft solder in this instance.

Reference to Fig. 7 will show that in the case of a cock with a weight driven barrel, instead of the great wheel, a large ratchet wheel is attached to the barrel. The ratchet, barrel, barrel cover, arbor assembly is anointed with soft solder paste along all the joints before assembling, and then heated with a modest flame. The solder will quickly flash through the joints, which should be almost push fits. Don't use too much solder paste - a little goes a long way.

On final assembly, make sure the small line hole in the barrel and the large hole in the ratchet wheel, through which the knot must pass, are adjacent. The outer surface of the barrel can be left smooth or a shallow "thread" can be cut in it to receive the line as it is wound. This is obviously done when initially machining the barrel. For an 8-day clock, sixteen turns are required of normally right hand thread of about 2 mm. pitch. Cut it with a round nosed tool having a tip radius of about 1.5 mm.; it need only be quite shallow. Emery it well to round off the peak of

Fig 14 : finishing small pieces.

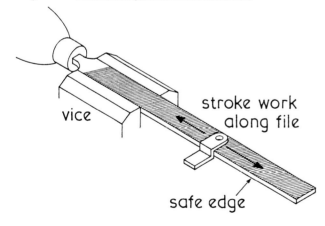

vice

stroke work along file

safe edge

filing buttons

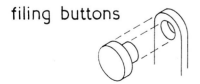

Fig 15: <u>weight drive barrel assembly.</u>

Fig 15A

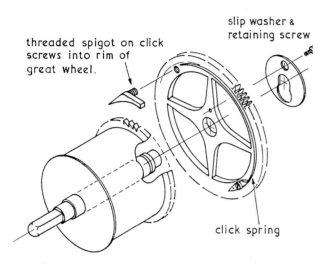

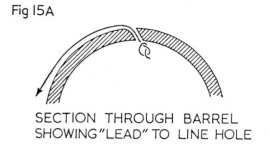

SECTION THROUGH BARREL
SHOWING "LEAD" TO LINE HOLE

the thread to avoid damaging the line. The line hole should lead into the thread so cut on the barrel surface - we want no sharp edge to cut into the line. See Fig. 15A.

The click is fitted to the rim of the great wheel as shown in Fig. 15. It can be secured with a shouldered screw as already described, but the threaded version shown is traditional on longcase clocks and it works well. The great wheel is secured on the arbor with a slip washer that fits a groove in the arbor. When fitted, the great wheel should be completely free to rotate, but should have minimal end play to avoid wobble. The slip washer can be dished somewhat to take up end play, if need be. To secure the washer, a 10 or 12BA cheese head screw is screwed fully into a tapped hole in the great wheel through a hole in the slip washer large enough to clear the screw head; the washer should be free to float slightly.

A month going skeleton timepiece using 2 spring barrels of moderate power, rather than 1 large and powerful spring.

Springs and Weights

When designing a new clock, there is no easy way of knowing exactly what size of spring or weight will be needed to drive it. Experience is usually the best guide. With any published design the size of spring or weight will be specified; if you are designing your own clock, or restoring a movement where the driving force is missing, you will just have to experiment a little.

Determining weight required is easy. Set the clock up on a test stand and wind a short length of line onto the barrel. Tie a wire hook on the free end of the line and hang a supermarket plastic bag from it. Start to fill the bag up with tins of baked beans, cat food etc. until there is enough weight just to keep the clock going. The weights can then be read off the labels, and added together. The actual weight required to drive the clock reliably is typically 1¼ to 1½ times this total. If the clock weight is fitted with a pulley to double the going period, then the weight must also be doubled. Weights can be solid brass, steel, cast iron, or lead, but on quality clocks they are usually made by fitting end caps to a brass cylinder filled with lead. As a guide to the volume required, lead weighs just over 11 grams/cubic centimetre, while steel and brass both weigh about 8 grams/cc.

In selecting a spring for a going barrel or fusee clock you have three main dimensions to be concerned with: the inside diameter of the barrel, the width of the spring, and its thickness. Clockmakers refer to the width of the spring as its height, and the the thickness as its "force", or "strength". These terms might seem a little odd to a non-clockmaker,

Fig 16.
lead filled brass weight.

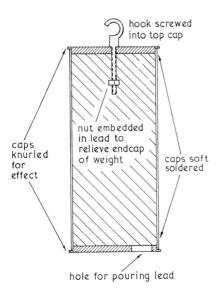

hook screwed into top cap

nut embedded in lead to relieve endcap of weight

caps knurled for effect

caps soft soldered

hole for pouring lead

particularly the words "force" or "strength" for what is really a linear measurement, but they are universally understood by both professional and amateur clockmakers, so I will continue to use them here. The thickness of a clock spring is the one measurement which most affects its power output, and it is probably from this that the term force, or strength, came to be used by clockmakers, centuries ago.

The first spring driven clocks, in the 16th century, were horizontal table clocks - i.e. they were designed to sit in the same position as a pocket watch placed flat on a table. It is therefore easy to see why early clockmakers referred to height as what one might today want to call the width of a spring. With the spring in that position, it would have been logical enough to refer to the spring's vertical dimension as its height.

The length does not really affect the power output and is not usually specified. It does affect the going period, but a spring designed for a 50 mm. barrel, for instance, will be of the correct length for that barrel diameter, and should occupy 50% of the volume of the barrel, excluding the volume occupied by the arbor. This condition obviously applies whether the spring is fully wound or completely relaxed within the barrel, and gives the optimum turns/power ratio for the spring. It follows that a strong spring will develop fewer turns in a given barrel diameter than a less powerful one. This is taken into account when designing the clock.

The potential power output of a spring is a product of its height and force, and is directly proportional to the height, and to the cube of its force. As an example, a spring with a height of 20 mm. and a force of 0.35 mm. results in a figure of 0.8575, the product of 20×0.35^3. This result is not an expression of torque in gram-cms. or in in.-lbs. (a lot more mathematics and knowledge of the spring's properties are required for that), but simply a figure for comparison. A spring of similar height but with a force of 0.4 mm. would produce a value of 20×0.4^3 = 1.28. 1.28 divided by 0.8575 = 1.49, which indicates an increase in power of 49% for an increase in force of just 14%. If we wanted to have the same increase in power while keeping the force at 0.35 mm., the height would have to be increased to 30 mm.

The side clearance of a spring within its barrel should be between 1 and 2mm, to ensure that the spring winds cleanly, but without tendency to twist or bunch, and this should be borne in mind if changing spring sizes.

Maintaining Power

Mention was made earlier of maintaining power, a device to prevent the train of a weight driven or fusee clock from running backwards when being wound. Fig. 17 shows the principle of the arrangement. This particular version is known as Harrison's Maintaining Power, after its inventor, John Harrison, who also won the Admiralty prize for solving the problem of timekeeping at sea. There are many variations on this same basic theme.

The barrel contains an integral ratchet as usual, but the driving or going click, instead of being fitted to the great wheel, is fitted to a second ratchet which is quite free on the barrel arbor. This maintaining ratchet is prevented from turning backwards by a second maintaining click pivoted between the plates. Between the maintaining ratchet and the great wheel is an annular space containing the maintaining spring. A pin in the maintaining ratchet pushes the spring forward when the clock is going, while the other end of the spring bears on a pin in the great wheel. The spring is compressed and drives the great wheel forward. During winding, the weight drive is taken off the ratchet but the maintaining spring continues to drive the great wheel and the rest of the train.

The maintaining spring does not have enough power actually to drive the clock, but it is sufficient to keep the train turning for several minutes, while the pendulum's own momentum keeps it swinging.

The pin in the great wheel extends into a slot in the ratchet, and when going, the ratchet drives this pin directly, but when the drive is removed (i.e. when the clock is being wound), the spring takes over the provide power to the great wheel. The other end of the slot prevents the great wheel pin from losing contact with the spring and limits relative movement between wheel and ratchet to about 15°. These drive pins are best made from steel, and should be fairly substantial, say about 2mm diameter. They could be of silver steel, hardened and tempered.

The maintaining spring can be cut from gauge plate, or bent up from silver steel wire, and then hardened and tempered. I find them to be a little too stiff when these materials are used, however, and I prefer to make them from "piano wire" in its as-purchased state. It is sufficiently springy to serve the purpose, but is easily bent to shape with pliers and formers.

Fig 17 : Harrison's maintaining power.

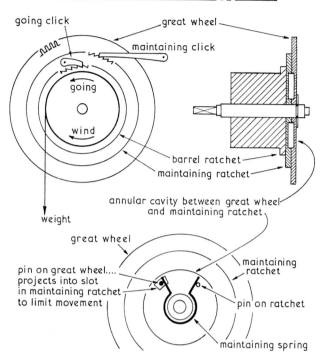

A Fusee Engine for cutting the groove in the fusee after turning it to profile in the lathe. The spare arbor is for cutting a different pitch thread on the fusee - see pages 23 to 25.

Fusees

The fusee is used in spring driven clocks to even out the power delivered by the spring. It is seldom used today except in high class work, although it is often used by amateur clockmakers in skeleton clocks. It is traditional in English skeleton clocks and English Dial clocks. The wisdom of its use with the recoil escapement - which is in fact the escapement it is most commonly used with - is a little debatable, as the errors inherent in recoil escapements tend to cancel out the errors introduced by the decreasing power of the spring as it unwinds. A fusee will improve the performance of a recoil escapement, but not always in proportion to the extra work involved in making a fusee instead of a going barrel.

I would not necessarily recommend a fusee clock as a first attempt in clockmaking, as it is a lot more work than a going barrel movement. However, a description of it will not come amiss here, as I am sure you will be tempted sooner or later.

Fig. 18 shows the principle of the fusee arrangement, as well as the necessary stopwork to prevent the line being wound off the small end of the fusee.

The working should be fairly obvious from the drawing. When the clock is run down, all the line is on the barrel. When the clock is wound via the winding square on the fusee, the line is wound off the spring barrel and onto the fusee from the large end to the small end, and at the same time this winding action winds up the spring. When fully wound, the spring exerts its force (via the fusee line) on the small end of the fusee, but as it runs down, the diminishing power of the spring pulls the line from an increasing radius of the fusee, thus giving a greater mechanical advantage, and thus keeping the torque supplied by the great wheel to the train fairly constant.

I say "fairly constant" because, for best results, the curve of the fusee needs to be matched to the particular spring with which it will work. This can be a longwinded process involving setting the spring up with a "standard" fusee, measuring the torque at each turn of winding, doing some sums, and then making the actual fusee to match the spring. My own opinion is that it is not worth the effort involved. If you want precision timekeeping, use a weight drive. Nevertheless, the fusee is an attractive device particularly in skeleton clocks.

Projecting radially from the small end of the fusee is a steel or brass arm called the stop arm. A cock attached to the plate has the fusee iron pivoted in it

Fig 18 : <u>fusee work.</u>

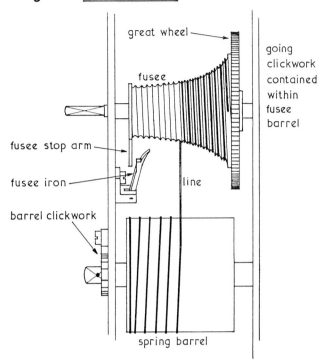

(this piece is viewed at an angle in Fig. 18). A wire or leaf spring (omitted from Fig. 18 for clarity) is also attached to the plate, and this spring keeps the fusee iron in the position shown. As the line is wound onto the fusee for the last two or three turns, it rides across the top of the fusee iron, and gradually pushes it down until it obstructs the passage of the stop arm. At this point the clock is fully wound and can be wound no more.

The clickwork is contained within an annular cavity, which can be in either the large end of the fusee, or in the great wheel. The click and spring are usually fixed within the cavity, and the ratchet is pinned or screwed to the other component, although it is sometimes done the other way around. The great wheel is free on the arbor and is retained with a slip washer in the same way as on a weight driven clock.

Maintaining power can also be applied to fusee cocks. The maintaining ratchet is interposed between the fusee and great wheel in the same way as for weight barrels. The fusee going clickwork obviously drives the maintaining ratchet instead of the great wheel.

The spring barrel is quite free to rotate on its arbor, but is prevented from doing so by the spring. The arbor is squared on the end, both to receive a ratchet and to allow it to be turned with a key to "set up" the spring. Fusee work can be tricky to set up. (It can be even trickier to let down!) One seems to need three hands. When assembling the clock, the line is completely wound off both fusee and barrel. The barrel click is disengaged, and the barrel is rotated to wind the line onto it; the click is then re-engaged with the ratchet. This click does not have a spring, but can be kept in engagement with a finger while the barrel arbor is wound up about one full turn. This is the "spring set up". One turn is usually about right; some clocks need more, some less.

If you have gone to the trouble of matching the fusee curve to the spring, then this set up should duplicate the degree of set up used when the spring and fusee were tested, and the same requirement will apply every time the clock is taken down and reassembled. Once the spring has been set up, the barrel click screw can be tightened to hold the click securely; it will not need to move again until the clock is next taken down for cleaning or repair. The barrel click screw does not need to be shouldered as in going barrel clickwork.

The object of setting up the spring is to use only the middle turns, where the torque is most uniform, to drive the clock. The spring is never completely relaxed within the barrel, neither is it wound to the point of being "coil bound", which it can be - and quite often is - in a going barrel not provided with stopwork.

The construction of a fusee is fairly straightforward. The fusee is permanently fixed to its arbor. Traditionally, the arbor was made slightly tapered and driven into the fusee blank and then arbor and fusee were turned as a single unit. I prefer to make the two items separately and unite them permanently with one of the modern glues such as Araldite or Loctite, the latter being my personal choice. They can also be soft soldered together, but the glue method is easier to clean up, and any surplus glue can be wiped off, before it sets, using a solvent such as white spirit or lighter fuel.

The fusee arbor is turned from silver steel, and is a job similar to making a barrel arbor, which we have already dealt with.

The piece of large diameter brass rod from which the fusee will be turned is first chucked in the 3-jaw and the end faced. This will be the large end, in which the recess for the clickwork is cut, so now is the time to machine this recess. The centre hole can also be drilled through at the same time. The blank is then reversed in the chuck and faced off to length. A service arbor is then turned from a piece of 12mm

BDMS rod. Centre drill the end, support it with the tailstock centre and turn down enough length for a good fit right through the fusee blank. Then produce a thread on the outboard end for a nut and washer to hold the blank, either by screwcutting, or by means of a threading die. Mount the fusee blank on the service arbor for profiling.

The profile of the fusee curve can be turned by eye against a template cut from thin sheet metal or even wood, but a more satisfactory way is to first draw the profile say 5 times full size on a piece of graph paper. It is then easy to work out a series of co-ordinates for cross feed and linear feed - e.g.

> 1st cut: feed in .5mm and along 30mm
> 2nd cut: feed in .5mm and along 27mm
> and so on.

Try to keep the cross feed the same every time. These incremental cuts will produce a very close approximation of the fusee profile in the form of a series of small steps, which can then easily be cut to a smooth profile with a round graver (see Fig. 6).

Fig 19: fusee grooving engine.

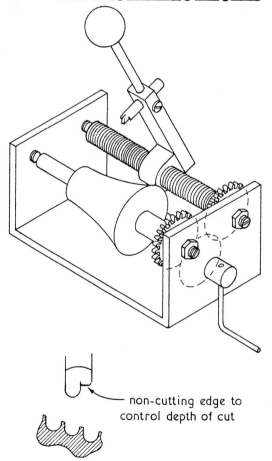

non-cutting edge to control depth of cut

profile of cutter & groove formed

As the fusee is made from a free cutting brass, you will need to raise the handle end of the graver up to give the cutting edge a lot of negative rake. Once you get the hang of it, the job can be done without a tool rest - you'll be surprised how fast the chips fly! Be careful though - remove the lathe tool from the toolpost and move the saddle well out of the way.

Now for the groove. Your first thought will probably be to use the lathe in screwcutting mode, but you will have to make some sort of hinged or sliding toolholder that can follow the curve. Backlash is a problem, plus there is a tendency to chatter. I spent an evening making a sliding toolholder but was not happy with the end result when using it. I found it best to turn the lathe by hand, but this is at best a cumbersome procedure, so I made the little "fusee engine" shown in Fig. 19.

This item is well worth the effort of making it, as cutting the groove then becomes a smooth and fairly quick job. The follower thread (a piece of studding) is easily changed if you require a different pitch for the groove on the next fusee you make.

The fusee groove is a normal right hand thread, and is best cut "downhill", from the large to the small end. The cutter is shaped to ride on the "land" between the grooves when they are cut to full depth, thus ensuring constant groove depth.

On some old clocks, the fusee stop arm is an integral part of the fusee, which was made from a casting, but often it was a separate piece made from steel rather than brass, and secured with a couple of countersunk screws into the end of the fusee. This is the easier way of doing it.

Little comment is required on the barrel or barrel arbor. Both barrel covers are identical, with the exception that one has a small cut-out in the rim to accommodate the fusee line knot. The rim of the barrel has a hole or holes to thread the line through. Most fusee spring barrels on older clocks will be found to have one cover soft soldered in place, as is the great wheel in a going barrel. You may wish to do it this way, or to make them both detachable, as is more commonly done today.

Stopwork

We have already discussed fusee stopwork to some degree. There are other mechanisms which can be used on going barrel and weight driven clocks to prevent "overwinding". The most common is the "Maltese Cross" type - see Fig. 20. In a going barrel movement the finger washer fits over a square on the barrel arbor, and is stationary on the arbor (it only moves when winding). The barrel rotates clockwise. The cross rotates on a shouldered screw set either in the barrel end cap or in the great wheel - either way will work fine. As the cross crosses the finger, it also rotates clockwise as the finger engages one of the slots. After the designed number of turns, the finger comes up against that part of the cross with no slot and the barrel, or arbor, can rotate no further.

The spring needs to be set up a turn or two against the stopwork before being put into the movement. The idea, as with fusee set up, is to use the middle turns of the spring to drive the clock.

In a weight driven movement, stopwork is used simply to prevent the weight being wound up so far as to bump it into the seatboard or the bottom of the movement, thus straining the line.

In a weight driven movement fitted with the "Maltese Cross" stopwork mechanism, the cross would be mounted on a screw set in the clock plate, and would rotate in the opposite direction to the barrel arbor and barrel, both of which rotate clockwise when the clock is being wound, and anti-clockwise when the clock is going. If you wish to use stopwork in a weight driven movement, the easier-to-make option is the fusee type. In fact it is rare to find stopwork fitted to a weight movement.

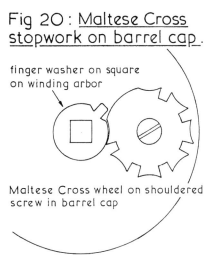

Fig 20 : <u>Maltese Cross stopwork on barrel cap</u>.

finger washer on square on winding arbor

Maltese Cross wheel on shouldered screw in barrel cap

Arbors & Pivots

This subject and its relevance to the heavy barrel arbor has already been dealt with, but the much finer pivots found further up the train demand a different technique. The intermediate (or "8 day") arbor in 8-day clocks is often large enough to be dealt with in the same way as the barrel arbor, but from the centre wheel upwards the pivots are best turned, or in any case, most certainly finished, between centres in the clockmaker's "throw", the work being done by the use of gravers.

A clockmaker's throw is a motorised version of the old clockmaker's "turns", and the basics of it are illustrated in Fig. 21. It is not a difficult or time-consuming tool to make, and once you have it you will wonder how you ever managed without it! Many accessories can be made for the clockmaker's throw, such as the Jacot tool (for pivot filing and dressing) and a tailstock drilling jig for drilling down the centre of an arbor, which is necessary when re-pivoting a clock that has come in for repair. (Drilling between centres? Yes! More anon.)

When you are using a graver, cutting silver steel demands a little more care than does cutting brass. The graver must be presented to the work with positive top rake. When cutting up to a shoulder, the very tip of the tool is used. If not done carefully, this can lead to a dig-in, which will do neither the workpiece, the tool tip, nor your nerves, any good.

The best idea is to practise on a piece of scrap silver steel, say 2 mm. diameter, until you feel ready to

Fig 21: the clockmakers' throw.

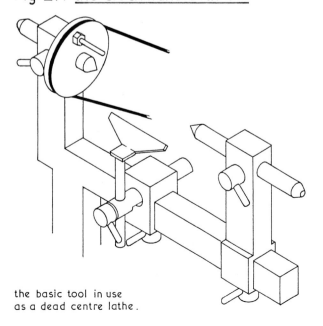

the basic tool in use
as a dead centre lathe.

tackle the actual job. Practise turning down to a smaller diameter for just a short distance (as if turning a pivot). Also practise reducing the diameter perhaps not so much, but for about 30 mm. along the piece, keeping the new diameter parallel. The knack is soon acquired. The metal is shaved off rather than cut off, and you will only be removing about a thou (or less) at a time.

As previously remarked, the cutting edge of the graver is presented to the work with plenty of top rake, and at about 30° to the axis of the workpiece.

Use the point of the graver to cut a little groove as a starting point where the shoulder of the pivot will be, leaving a tiny amount to be cut back later to bring the arbor to length. Set the tool rest at a comfortable height, which will probably be about 8 or 10 mm. below the workpiece centre line, and about 10 mm. off the work. The right hand controls the angle and contact of the graver, while the thumb and first fingers of the left hand hold the graver against the tool rest and slowly move it from left to right to shave off the metal. It is quite easy to shave off "tenths" when aiming for a wringing or drive fit for a collet, etc.

The old clockmakers used to put a male centre on both ends of the embryo arbor before turning. On some old clocks, the ends of the pivots are still pointed from this operation. These male centres were not turned on a lathe but were done by twisting the arbor between the fingers while resting one end on the edge of a small block of wood and running a file across it. I prefer to cut the piece of bar for the arbor about 4 mm. over length and put a female centre in each end. Putting a female centre in the end of a piece of 2 mm. diameter material may sound tricky, but the tool illustrated in Fig. 22 will enable you to do it in seconds on the throw. It does not need to be more than 1 mm. deep, if that. When the arbor is finished, the excess length is cut or filed off, and the end of the pivot is domed and polished, giving a nice finished look to the part.

The final shape of the pivot and shoulder is important. The objective is to reduce friction to a minimum. The pivot portion must be parallel and highly polished. The internal angle between pivot and shoulder must be square and sharp, and the outer edge of the shoulder should be chamfered to reduce the area of shoulder in contact with the plate around the pivot hole.

In spite of ample endshake, a lot of friction - and therefore power loss - can be caused at this point, so

Fig 22 : <u>centre drilling attachment for the throw.</u>

workpiece, driven from headstock catchplate.

hardened & polished silver steel centre drilled plug.
drive fit in tube.

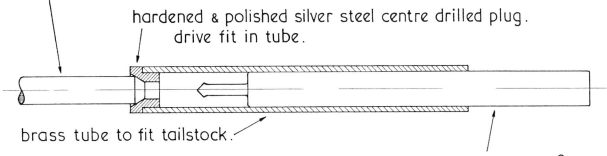

brass tube to fit tailstock.

centre drill, sliding fit through tube. form spade bit with 90°
inclusive angle.   harden, do not temper.

the shoulder should also be polished. When you consider that the overall gear ratio between the spring barrel and escape wheel of an 8-day clock is often well over 1:3,000, you will understand the reason for minimising all possible sources of friction. (On a month going clock this ratio can easily be as high as 1:15,000!)

This may be a good point at which to discuss the pivot hole in the brass plate, in which the steel pivot runs. The first important thing to note is that the hole is not parallel! The hole is initially drilled undersize, and then opened out from both ends with a taper broach until the pivot "falls" home freely, with just 1° or 2° of sideplay or "wobble". The pivot must be absolutely free, but should have the minimum amount of sideshake in the hole. The reason for the tapered hole is twofold:-

1. When assembling the clock, it is often necessary when fitting the second plate to have to locate the pivots one at a time, particularly in an older clock, because the pivots will be slightly floppy in their holes in the other plate, and therefore do not all stand up nice and straight. The plates are obviously not parallel at this stage, and therefore the pivots are slightly out of the perpendicular to this plate until it is finally pushed down onto the ends of the pillars. The slight taper to the holes assists this assembly procedure. Having said that, it should also be noted that when assembling on a level surface, it is quite possible - even likely - that the second plate will sit right down over all the pivots and pillars with no "fiddling" at all. One gets a great feeling of satisfaction with a job well done when that happens!

2. We are back to the problem of reducing friction: with the hole tapered from both ends, the pivot is bearing on a very small area near the centre of the hole. Wear will eventually increase this bearing area, but at least we start off with the ideal.

Fig. 23 is a section through this ideal pivot bearing, although the taper is exaggerated for clarity. Note the chamfer on the shoulder of the pivot and the slight countersink to the hole, all aimed at reducing friction. The oil sink is a large, shallow countersink, with a concave surface. Simple cutters to form oil sinks can be made in the form of a round-ended D-bit; make from silver steel, hardened and tempered. Polish the cutting end, so that it will give a good finish to the sink.

Pivots, and indeed the whole arbor, can be hardened and tempered if you wish. If the pinion is separate from the arbor, it is sufficient to harden only the ends - i.e. only the pivots. If the pinion is integral

Fig 23: <u>section through pivot.</u>

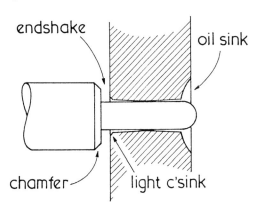

with the arbor (in which case the whole thing is called the pinion!) then the usual practice is to harden the entire piece from end to end.

In quenching, to minimise the risk of distortion from rapid cooling, you should ensure that the arbor falls into the quenching medium vertically.

Hardening is not obligatory (polishing is far more important), but it obviously extends the wear life of the item. However, I think that unhardened silver steel will have a surprisingly long and satisfactory life. I rarely harden pivots, except for those under particularly heavy stress, such as the gathering pallet arbor in strikework.

Finally, the pivot holes in the plates should be burnished. This polishes and work hardens the brass, which will extend the life of the bearing. Smoothing broaches can be purchased with the same taper as cutting broaches, but I use cheap and readily available sewing and darning needles! Work the needle backwards and forwards and also around the hole with as much pressure as you can without breaking the needle. A little oil on the needle will keep it from "picking up".

Pivot Polishing and the Jacot Tool

The best tool for finishing pivots is known as a Jacot tool. It is illustrated in Fig. 24, and is essentially a small tailstock turret with a series of semi-circular beds to rest the pivot in while using the pivot file and burnisher. It can be made for use in the bench lathe, but if you have made a throw, then make it as an accessory for this, which will increase the versatility of that tool.

In use, the arbor is supported in a female centre in the headstock, while the pivot being treated is rested in a suitable diameter bed on the brass drum. A single roller filing rest is put in the toolpost, and the pivot file is then run across the pivot, followed by emery sticks.

The arbor is driven by the catchplate (or "ferrule" as it is called on the throw or turns). There is obviously a tendency for the pivot to climb out of the bed when free of the pressure from the pivot file etc. I use a piece of wood dowel about 150 mm. long x 4 or 5 mm. diameter to apply a restraint to the arbor to prevent this from happening. I hold the dowel in my left hand from behind the throw; a small notch near the tip of the dowel prevents it slipping off the arbor. This way it does not hinder access to the pivot being worked on. The pivot is treated first with the pivot file, then with fine emery sticks, and finally with a square or flat burnisher. Brush the emery dust out of the bed before using the next finest tool, and use motor oil to lubricate the burnisher.

The end of the pivot is rounded off with the file and emery sticks, and then burnished. This is done by using the disc tool instead of the Jacot drum. The pivot protrudes through one of the holes in the disc, but obviously must not make contact with the disc, or the polishing you have done will be ruined. The chamfer on the shoulder of the pivot bears on the countersink around the hole in the disc and takes the pressure of the drive and the filing operation.

A final burnish needs to be given to the pivot without the bearing surface having contact with anything other than the burnisher. This is done by using the half female centre runner also illustrated in Fig. 24. Rest the pivot end as far up the centre as it will go to run smoothly, and then lightly run a very fine and worn emery stick over it a couple of times, before finishing with a flat or oval burnisher. I prefer the oval burnisher for this last operation; with some care the point of the burnisher can be brought right up to the shoulder. Also, since the contact area is small, it does not take much force to put considerable pressure on the surface of the pivot. Move it along slowly so as not to show up a "thread".

When all of the above has been done properly, you should be able to see your face in the surface of the pivot!

Fig 24 : the Jacot Tool .

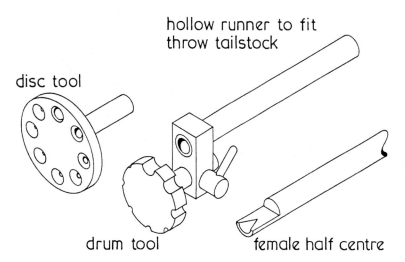

hollow runner to fit throw tailstock

disc tool

drum tool

female half centre

By way of a slight digression, the disc tool can also be used for drilling the end of an arbor for fitting a new pivot, to replace a damaged one. Having removed the remains of the damaged pivot, the end of the arbor is filed flat and square to the axis, and a centre made with the drill in Fig. 22. The Jacot tool is then set up with the arbor located in a suitable hole in the disc, and carefully centred with the aid of a pointed centring rod put through the hollow runner of the tool (for useful interchangeability, the bore through the runner should be the same as that of the drill runner).

The required hole can then be drilled with a standard twist drill. Fit one of your throw's workpiece carriers to the drill to stop it from turning, back it into the hollow runner, and then locate the business end in the workpiece centre. Another rod, this time with a female centre, is then put through the runner from the back end to apply pressure to the drill. You will have an absolutely concentric hole, and all done between centres. (Who needs a chuck?!) Use a sewing or darning needle for the new pivot. They are already hardened, tempered and polished. Choose a size that is a light drive fit for the hole you have drilled (or vice versa). The hole depth should be about 1½ times the length of the working pivot.

I think that the final word on pivoting has to be the word "freedom". A clock train must have absolute freedom of movement. There can be no "running in", as there is just not enough power to spare. On the average size clock built by the amateur, there should be about 0.3 to 0.5 mm. endshake in all pivots, and the minimum of sideshake consistent with complete freedom. If the clock is lying on its back and slowly lifted and tilted over onto its front, all the pivots should audibly drop to the front plate long before the horizontal position is reached. When pressure is applied to the barrel or great wheel, the escape wheel (without the pallets in place) should spin freely, and its momentum should drive the train for several seconds before everything slowly coasts to a halt.

The need for this sort of smooth freedom cannot be stressed enough. The slightest stiffness, a bent or damaged tooth, or incorrectly meshed teeth, even at the "heavy" end of the train, will stop the clock.

A clockmakers' throw (miniature dead centre lathe) shown with some associated tooling and set up with the JACOT tool for pivot polishing.

Wheels and Pinions

Although wheelcutting was dealt with briefly in connection with the barrel or great wheel, it is now time to deal with it in more detail.

The wheels and pinions are the heart of the clock, and if not cut and meshed, or "depthed", correctly, can use up an awful lot of power, of which, as just discussed, there is no surplus.

Clocks use cycloidal gearing, this being the most efficient form where the smaller wheel is the driven one, and the ratio is high. In clocks, it can be 1:10, or even higher, in one step. I am not going to delve into the theory of gearing - more learned men than I have done so, and literature is available for those interested. I will deal with the important practical points as they arise.

There are probably half a dozen or so variations on the basic tooth form used in clockwork today. In the past there were more, each country, district, or even manufacturer having a favourite tooth profile for wheels and pinions. Luckily for us, they nearly all seem to mesh with each other well enough not to cause any great problem when we have to cut a new wheel for an old clock, although with a valuable clock one really ought to make a special "one off" cutter to match the profile of the existing teeth.

There are two systems used in the design of gear trains, the Imperial "Diametral Pitch" (D.P.) system, and the metric "Module" (M) system. As the Module system is virtually universal in clockwork, I do not propose to discuss the D.P. system at all. The Module is a much easier system to work with, and as I work 100% metric when designing clocks, using

the Module system for the gears is much simpler. (Having said that, I shall also freely confess that I prefer the Imperial system when designing and making wooden clock cases!)

The Module of a wheel (or "gear" as an engineer would call it) is defined as the pitch circle diameter (PCD) of the wheel divided by the number of teeth in that wheel. A wheel of 48 teeth with a PCD of 48 mm. will be Module 1.0 (M 1.0). A wheel of 48 teeth of M 0.8 would have a PCD of 38.4 mm. (= 48 x 0.8).

The profiles of the teeth in both wheels and pinions are in direct relation to the Module number involved, and any dimension can be quickly calculated by multiplying the factor concerned by the Module number. Figs. 25 and 26 show the profiles and factors for wheel and pinion teeth, and the simplicity of the system should become clear from a study of these diagrams.

Wheels are generally regarded as having 20 teeth or more, and pinions as having 16 teeth or less. (As for one with 18 teeth, it would depend on its duty and whether it was driving or being driven.) The tooth forms shown in Figs. 25 and 26 are the nearest we seem to have to a standard profile, and they will be found to mesh in a satisfactory manner with almost any other clock wheel/pinion you are likely to encounter.

Strictly speaking, the wheel tooth profile should change slightly depending on the number of teeth in the wheel, and if you purchase commercial multi-tooth cutters, your wheel tooth profiles will exhibit this admirable quality. However, if you prefer to make your own single point flycutters, as I do, fear not. A cutter made to cut the profile shown will be fine for all tooth counts above 40 or so. Counts below this number are more likely to be found on motion work etc. where the duty is very light, and efficient power transmission not particularly important. The same cutter will do a satisfactory job in this case.

Study of Fig. 25 will show that the sides of the teeth

Fig 25 : wheel tooth profile.

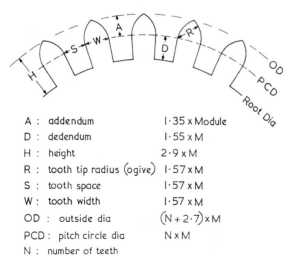

A :	addendum	1·35 x Module
D :	dedendum	1·55 x M
H :	height	2·9 x M
R :	tooth tip radius (ogive)	1·57 x M
S :	tooth space	1·57 x M
W :	tooth width	1·57 x M
OD :	outside dia	(N + 2·7) x M
PCD :	pitch circle dia	N x M
N :	number of teeth	

Fig 26 : pinion tooth profile.

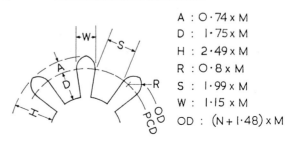

A :	0·74 x M
D :	1·75 x M
H :	2·49 x M
R :	0·8 x M
S :	1·99 x M
W :	1·15 x M
OD :	(N + 1·48) x M

within the dedendum space are radial to the wheel, and this of course is the ideal. However, another small compromise here will do no harm - when making the cutter (and remember: the cutter cuts spaces, not teeth), make it to cut the dedendum space with parallel sides. This makes the teeth a couple of "thou" narrower at the root than on the PCD, but in practice this is of very little consequence in terms of the strength of the tooth, and the cutter will cut the space more freely, as there will be no tendency for it to rub in the narrow angle.

The sort of flycutters we need can be filed up freehand with care, and if you are adept with needle files, this is the quickest way. Measure carefully as you go. They can be made on the lathe using a form tool, but if you do it that way, you must first make the form tool.

The form tool takes the shape of a parting tool with a tip radius equal to that of the ogive, and the cutter is formed with two plunge cuts as illustrated in Fig. 27A. The cutter should be tilted about 10° away from the side being cut, to provide the necessary side clearance.

If you can file the cutter to shape by hand satisfactorily, it is probably the quicker approach, so it is a skill well worth developing. Make them from silver steel of a diameter (probably 5 or 6 mm.) to suit the hole in the arbor in your flycutting frame, and harden and temper them to dark straw. Such a cutter will produce the teeth on dozens of brass wheels before it needs re-sharpening. Make them with zero or even negative top rake, but plenty of

side and end clearance - at least 10°. Before hardening, get the best finish possible on the cutting edges by using fine oilstones or emery paper wrapped round a piece of wire, etc.

The finer the finish on the tool, the better the finish on the wheel it cuts. Run these cutters at 5000 to 6000 rpm. You will be surprised how quickly they cut, but wear eye protection, as the chips fly everywhere.

In motion work there are usually two meshing equal count wheels, the cannon and the reverse minute wheel. Fig. 25 shows that the tooth width and tooth space on the PCD are equal, and therefore if the wheels are correctly depthed, the freedom between them will be eliminated, and the teeth can even jam. There is almost no stress on these wheels, so the teeth can be cut slightly narrower, thereby making the space slightly wider, to give freer movement.

There are two ways of doing this. The ratio between these two wheels is 1:1, and the number of teeth usually 39. The first method is to cut the blank to the OD for the nominal module with 39 teeth, but to cut 40 teeth. The space will be to module size, but the teeth will be narrower by the ratio of 39/40. This will probably be just enough to allow sufficient freedom.

The other method, which I prefer, is to turn the blank to the correct OD for the module and number of teeth wanted, but to use a cutter of Module 0.05 larger than nominal - i.e. if the nominal module is 0.6 then use a M 0.65 cutter. This both increases the space and narrows the tooth. The result will be freely meshing wheels with non-critical depthing, and you can concentrate on getting correct depthing for the reverse minute pinion and the hour wheel.

Fig. 26 shows that pinion teeth are of a different and

Fig 27 :

single point flycutters for brass wheels.
for use in the flycutting frame :Fig 12

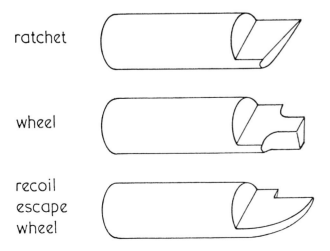

ratchet

wheel

recoil
escape
wheel

Fig 27A MAKING FLYCUTTERS

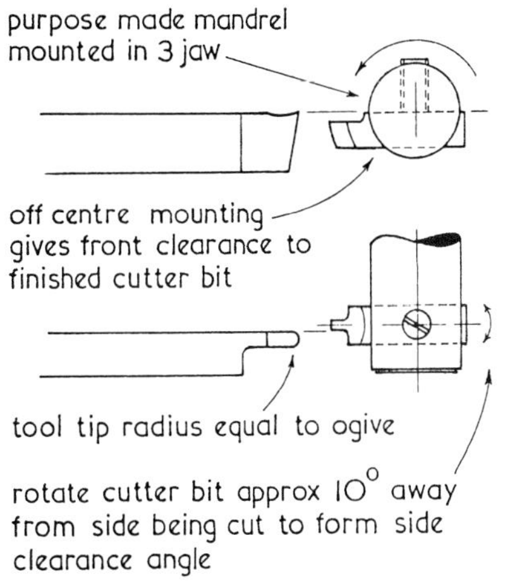

purpose made mandrel
mounted in 3 jaw

off centre mounting
gives front clearance to
finished cutter bit

tool tip radius equal to ogive

rotate cutter bit approx 10° away
from side being cut to form side
clearance angle

smaller profile than wheel teeth. While pinions can be cut with a single point cutter, it is a slow process, and you will find that multi-tooth, form-relieved cutters cut much quicker and cleaner. Remember that in making pinions, we are cutting silver steel and even the free cutting variety is inclined to be a little "sticky". If you have made your own multi-tooth cutters before, or feel confident that you can do so, then there is no reason not to, but I think most of us, myself included, prefer to buy these from a commercial source.

They are expensive, but they will last indefinitely, and can be re-sharpened with the correct grinding wheel and jig. Just buy them as you need them, and you will soon have a useful collection.

You will need a different cutter for each different pinion you wish to cut, not only the module size, but also the number of teeth. In an emergency, you can cut a 7 leaf pinion with a cutter designed for 6 leaves of the same module (or 8 with 7 etc.) but I stress that this is for emergencies only.

In comparing the tip radius of wheel and pinion teeth, it will be noticed that on wheels this radius is equal to the tooth width. This is known as the full ogive form. On the pinion shown in Fig. 26, this radius is somewhat less than tooth width, and is known as ⅓ ogive, the radius being struck from a point roughly that fraction of the tooth width along the PCD.

To have a more nearly theoretically correct profile, pinions of 6 and 7 leaves should have full ogive, 8 and 9 leaves ⅓ ogive, and 10 leaves or more a half-round tip profile, the radius being struck from the centre of the tooth width on the PCD.

If you buy commercial cutters, you will find they obey this rule, but if you make your own you will get quite satisfactory results by making them all to the ⅓ ogive form. Clock designers and manufacturers in the past have used the ⅓ ogive profile for all pinions no matter what the tooth count, and the result has been quite satisfactory in terms of both wear and power transmission. In making a "one-off" clock, the wheels and pinions are individually depthed (we will come to that subject shortly) in any case, to give the optimum centre distance for free running and minimum friction.

The cutting of wheels has been dealt with briefly but this would seem a good point at which to explain some of the finer points in more detail, for the benefit of those who may not yet have tried it. If you

have a dividing attachment for your lathe headstock, or a dividing head for use on the lathe or on the milling machine, then I will assume you will use whichever method applies in your case. The next few paragraphs are for those who are starting from scratch with no dividing equipment.

It is an obvious advantage if the wheel blank can be mounted on a mandrel in the lathe, so that the OD can be turned and the teeth cut without removing it from that mandrel. However, in order to do it this way, one must have some means of dividing one revolution of the lathe mandrel into the required number of steps for the tooth count(s) required. One way of doing this is to employ a suitable change wheel or other gear mounted on the outboard end of the mandrel, plus the provision of a detent to lock in between this gear's teeth. However, available change wheel counts have an unhappy knack of not coinciding with clock wheel counts. What we really need is a division plate which can be mounted in place of change wheels. A division plate is a metal disc of perhaps 150 mm. diameter with a series of concentric rings of holes of various counts. The plate is mounted on the outboard end of the lathe mandrel; a detent on a springy arm fixed to the bench or to a convenient part of the lathe then engages with a circle of holes of the required count, or a multiple of that count.

A useful series of index circles is: 144, 120, 100, 96, 90, 84, 80, 78, 70, 64, 62, 59... Counts such as 62 or 59 may seem a little odd, but when you want to do calendar or moon work, you will need them. It also follows that if you want to cut a wheel with, say, 60 teeth, then you index every second hole in the in the 120 index circle. 72, 48, 36, 24, 18, 16, 12, and 9 can all be indexed from the 144 circle, etc.

Fig. 28 shows the basic arrangement. Fig. 11 shows a suitable Morse taper mandrel for mounting in the lathe for holding the wheel blank. Always use a draw bar to secure the taper mandrel in your lathe spindle when wheelcutting, as the high frequency vibration of the cutting operation involved can cause it to work loose, causing spontaneous utterances such as "Oh deary me!" and "How unfortunate".

Division plates can be purchased, but sooner or later you are going to need a count that is not available. Or perhaps you would prefer to make your own plates anyway, for they are not cheap to buy. The following is one method of making quite accurate plates without the need to have access to a dividing head before you can make any sort of a start.

The first thing that is needed is a bandsaw blade, say

Fig 28: <u>dividing plate & wheel blank mounted on lathe.</u>

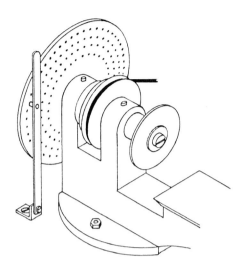

one about 8 or 10 mm. wide. A used blade is quite good enough, providing that if it has been re-sharpened, this has been done on a jig. If it has been re-sharpened by a professional saw doctor, this will be the case. The idea is to wrap a length of bandsaw blade, with the required number of teeth, around the circumference of a plywood disc to which our division plate blank is concentrically attached. The plywood disc can then be indexed around on the lathe spindle or on the drilling table, by means of the teeth in the blade, for drilling the index holes in the division plate. It may sound a little crude, but it works, and it is a very easy way to make satisfactory division plates.

Before proceeding further a little arithmetic is required. I shall assume that you wish to make a division plate of about 6″ diameter (I will use Imperial dimensions because bandsaw blades still seem to be make in "teeth per inch" sizes, and there seem to be two main sizes: 4 tpi and 10 tpi). If you are using a 10 tpi blade and wish to index 144 teeth by using every tooth, then the resulting circle of the blade will be only 4.58″diameter, which is too small. Therefore cut yourself enough bandsaw blade material to provide 288 teeth, and index every second tooth.

For this, the plywood disc on which the blade will nicely wrap will then be 9.16″ diameter (= 28.8″ ÷ π). For indexing 120, 100 etc. the piece of blade is shortened and the wood disc turned down to fit, but do your sums carefully first...... read on.
For 96 teeth (counting every second tooth) the circle

is 6.1″ diameter, too close to the diameter of the plate for comfort. However, 3 x 96 is 288, the same number as used for the 144 count. Therefore, with the same length of saw blade wrapped around the disc, we can index 144 by using every second tooth, and 96 by using every third tooth. For the 64 count circle of holes, we will need to reduce the length of blade to 25.8″ (= 256 + 2 teeth - see below for the reason for those two extra teeth), bring the disc to a shade under 8.15″diameter, and index every fourth tooth. By the time you get to the 120 and 80 counts, you will be getting the hang of it, and will know without being told that you will want only 24″ of blade length (plus the 2 extra teeth), and a disc OD a shade under 7.64″.

Make a table or chart of the counts you require and the resulting diameter of the circle made by the saw blade; it is then easy to see which index you need to use next, regardless of its final position on the dividing plate.

Now for the real work:

First, cut a disc of steel or brass about 5 mm. thick for the dividing plate. Put a centre punch mark in the centre and drill 3 holes at 120° on a PCD of about 60 or 70 mm. Set this aside for a few minutes.

Cut a disc of plywood about 15 mm. thick and a little larger than the maximum diameter you need. Screw or bolt it firmly to the lathe faceplate and take a skim across the face to ensure it is flat and true.

Now centre your division plate blank on the plywood disc with the tailstock centre in the centre punch mark, and apply 2 or 3 toolmakers' clamps to the assembly to immobilise it while you carefully run 3 screws through the division plate blank into the plywood.

The OD of the division plate can now be turned and the centre hole drilled and bored to fit the back end of your lathe mandrel (or to fit an expanding plug fitted in the mandrel bore). Bore this hole through the plywood also.

Next, the saw blade teeth. Assuming you wish to drill a 144 count on the division plate, cut off a piece of blade with 290 teeth on it - 288 for counting every second tooth, plus 2 more teeth for the overlap. Clean and tin the ends of the blade, turn it into a circle, overlap the 2 end teeth, and soft solder together. It is worth making a little wooden jig for this to ensure that the blade lies in a straight line at the joint. To maintain accuracy, you must take great care to ensure that the end 2 teeth overlap exactly.

Drill or punch a 1.5 mm. hole about 20 mm. away from the join. Now carefully turn down a shoulder on the outside of the plywood disc until the circle of saw blade will just push on to the disc - there must be no slack here. Turn the shoulder back just far enough to leave the teeth clear of the surface of the disc. Now, to make certain that the blade cannot move, drive a tapered clock pin through the little hole and into the disc.

If you have a toolpost drilling spindle, then the next job will be obvious to you - it simply remains to rig a temporary device (a piece of clock spring is ideal), to click into the saw teeth as you index around. It is also necessary to ensure that you take up any slack in your indexing device as you go around.

If you have to use the drilling machine to drill the holes in the division plate blank, then a little more work is required. Remove the faceplate assembly from the lathe, and install the 3-jaw to turn up a large bush. We will pivot the faceplate assembly on this bush on the drill press, so its diameter needs to be a nice shake-free fit in the centre hole in the division plate. It also needs to be long enough to pass through the faceplate, ply disc and division plate. Drill and countersink a hole through the centre to take a wood screw to fix it to a plywood baseboard which will be clamped to the drilling machine table. Fig. 29 illustrates all of the foregoing. Drill the indexing holes in the plate with a small cen-

tre drill. The holes are blind and only need to be about 1.5 mm. to 2 mm. deep. If you have depth stop on your drill press, use it. A wood block the same height as the faceplate spigot, placed under the edge of the faceplate, will take the pressure from the drilling. A piece of old clock spring, or a hacksaw blade, can be used as a detent to index the saw teeth.

Hold the assembly steady when drilling, and keep the saw tooth pushed back against the detent to ensure even spacing of the holes.

After the 144 hole circle and the 96 hole circle are drilled, the saw blade is taken off and shortened to the next count. The faceplate assembly is put back on the lathe to turn the shoulder down to suit, and so on. If your division plate is 5 or 6 mm. thick, and you are only drilling 2 - 3 mm. deep, then both sides of the plate can be used, as long as you stagger the rows on opposite sides of the plate. This way you can get at least 12 index circles on one 6" (150 mm.) plate.

Now, back to wheelcutting:

With the division plate and wheel blank on the lathe, mount the flycutting spindle on the vertical slide and rig up the drive. Make sure the cutter is perfectly centred above the centre line of the lathe, or you will cut "wolf's teeth". Adjust the height of the vertical slide to cut about half the depth of the tooth. Switch on and rack the saddle forward to cut the first space. Index for the next space, and cut it also.

Now lower the vertical slide slightly and cut both spaces again. Keep doing this, but be careful not to lower the slide too much as the cutter starts to shape the addendum. You will know you are cutting deep enough when there is just the tiniest witness of the wheel OD remaining at the tip of the addendum. Now lock the vertical slide and you can cut the rest of the teeth at one pass each.

Do not be tempted to pass the cutter through the first tooth space again when you get there. To do so would double any minute error which may have crept in through vibration or other sources.

The cutter will have thrown up small burrs on the back face of the teeth. The easiest way to remove these is with a fine file while running the lathe at a medium speed. Be careful just to touch the tooth, and not to mark the back face of the wheel.

Now comes one of the more routine bits of clockmaking, the job of "crossing out" the wheel. The crossings are not put in the wheels just to look

Fig 29 : drilling division plates in the drilling machine.

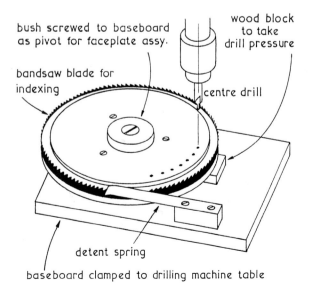

bush screwed to baseboard as pivot for faceplate assy.

wood block to take drill pressure

bandsaw blade for indexing

centre drill

detent spring

baseboard clamped to drilling machine table

pretty. They have the more important function of lowering mass and therefore inertia. The higher up the train you go, the more important this is. The escape wheel, for instance, has to accelerate and decelerate almost instantaneously. The lighter it is, the better it can fulfil this requirement.

Before you remove the wheel from the lathe, run the lathe and mark the OD of the crossings, i.e. the inside edge of the rim, with a scriber. Coat the wheel with marking out blue first, and you will hardly need to touch it to mark the line.

You can also index the outer ends of the crossings by means of the division plate, using a piece of wood in the toolpost as a guide for the scriber. There is no need to get these marks dead on centre height: just mark the point where the crossings meet the rim of the wheel. Four crossings is the usual number, but regulators and skeleton clocks sometimes have five or six. The higher number is usually the sign of better class work. Fig. 30 illustrates the two main types of crossing work.

The ID of the crossings - the hub of the wheel - is best marked out with the aid of a button. Turn about 6 mm. at the end of a piece of bar to the diameter required to mark out the wheel's ID, and then turn the last 1.5 mm. at the end down to a diameter just nicely to fit the existing hole of the wheel. Part the button off at about 5 mm. thick.

This button can be used to scribe the diameter on the wheel, and in the case of the "skeleton" type of crossing it can also be used as a filing guide by clamping it in the vice with the wheel. Keep these buttons - you may well need them again, whether on this clock or on another. For skeleton style crossings, it just remains to scribe the crossings themselves, with the aid of a rule laid across the wheel to connect the quarter points already marked, allowing for the width of the spoke itself, of course.

The traditional tapered spoke crossing is easily marked out with a cardboard template. Draw a freehand curve of the shape of one side of the crossing (use a French curve if you have a suitable one at hand), cut it to the shape and lay it on the wheel as a guide to scribe along.

When marking the first side of the first crossing, put a pencil dot, or a fine knife mark, on the template where it crosses the edge of the wheel; its posi-

tion can then be repeated, and if you transfer the dot to the other side of the template, it can be turned over to mark both sides of each crossing identically.

The traditional tool for cutting out crossings is the piercing saw. It is a good tool, is easy to keep close to the line, and leaves quite a good finish. An alternative, which I use, is the "Abrafile" or tension file. If you have not yet seen one of these, it is a piece of wire with teeth. It can be clamped in the piercing saw frame and used in the same way. It is quicker than the piercing saw, and less likely to break. It will also cut in any direction.

The job is made much easier if your fretsaw table has a clamp to hold the work. Fig. 31 shows a quickly made table to clamp in the bench vice. It can be made a convenient height at which to work standing up, which I find most convenient, as one can more easily move around the work.

Once the crossings are cut out, they are filed smoothly out to the scribed lines, and all corners are finished sharp. Finish all the edges created by crossing out work with ever finer pieces of emery wrapped around suitable needle files, until all file marks are obliterated and you have a nice shiny edge.

The edges of the crossings are then burnished to a mirror finish. This is quite easy to do on brass - the best tool to use is an old darning needle. Fit one into a pin chuck, or give it a small handle of its own, for ease of use. Using the pointed tip of the needle, you can burnish right up into the corners, to leave a mirror-like finish on all the crossings.

The burnishing will throw up a burr along the corners. Remove this with a scraper, but be careful

Fig 30 : wheel crossings.

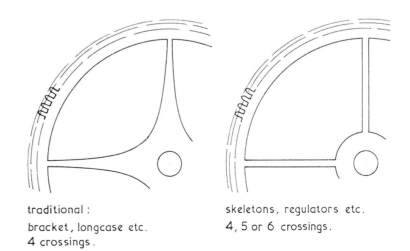

traditional :
bracket, longcase etc.
4 crossings .

skeletons, regulators etc.
4, 5 or 6 crossings .

not actually to bevel the edge. The most useful form of scraper is quickly made from an old three-square needle file. Carefully grind off the teeth to leave nice sharp hollow-ground edges. Sharpen by stoning each of the three flats on an oilstone. This tool can also be used in the initial stages of removing file marks from the crossings.

Finally, the faces of the wheel are polished by rubbing on ever-finer sheets of emery laid flat on the bench, on a surface plate, or on a piece of plate glass. By the time you get down to a piece of well worn 800 grit paper you should have a nice shiny finish. I usually go down to 1000 grit - again well worn - for polishing. Do not be tempted to use metal polish - not yet, anyway. I will cover this subject when we come to finishing.

Fig 31 : piercing saw table.

table from 6mm ply approx 250mm x 125mm

hardwood clamp

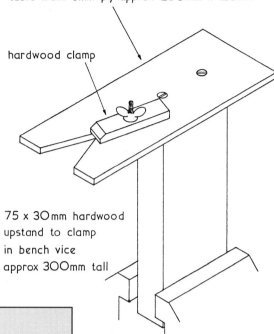

75 x 30mm hardwood
upstand to clamp
in bench vice
approx 300mm tall

A small dividing head for pinion cutting. The chuck is interchangeable between the head and the morse arbor. The head is fitted to the lathe vertical slide and the arbor, shown attached, fits the lathe headstock

Wheel Collets

The wheel has now to be mounted on its collet. Fig. 32 shows the two main designs of wheel collet. The collet itself is a simple job of brass turning. Turn the collet's wheel spigot (on the left in Fig. 32) to a slightly larger diameter than the hole in the centre of the wheel, and slightly longer than the thickness of the wheel.

Broach the wheel until it will go about half way onto the collet, and very lightly countersink the hole on both sides. Rest the collet in a good fitting hole in the bench stake, and tap the wheel down onto the shoulder with the aid of a hollow punch. The portion of the spigot protruding slightly beyond the wheel is then hammered down to fill the countersink and lock the wheel. Set the wheel/collet assembly in the 3-jaw chuck, holding by the collet, and skim the riveted face to tidy it up. Do not touch the face of the wheel.

The wheel should run true to the base of the collet; there should be no wobble or eccentricity.

The collet should be a free-running fit on its arbor at this stage, although you will probably have to run a drill or broach through it to open out the riveted end again. It can be fixed to the arbor with soft solder or with "Loctite". I prefer the latter, as it is easier to clean off excess. It can of course be made a force or drive fit, in which case the arbor is turned down carefully with a graver in the throw to a minute taper and the collet driven the last 5 - 6 mm. to its correct position. If using Loctite, put three or four marks around the arbor about 1 mm. in from where each end of the collet will fall in its final position. The collet should be a light push fit over these centre punch marks, and can be adjusted for true running, either by filing one or two of the centre punch marks down, or raising them by punching again.

When the wheel is running true, note its radial position on the arbor, take it off, coat the arbor with adhesive, and replace the wheel in the same

Fig 32 : wheel collets

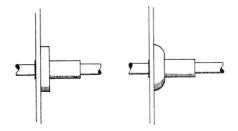

position. After about ten minutes the assembly can be handled safely, and semi-liquid excess adhesive outside the joint should then be wiped off with a cloth or tissue moistened with white spirit or lighter fluid.

The alternative method is to fix the collet firmly to the arbor by one of the above methods, before fixing the wheel to it. The arbor is then put in the throw, and the wheel seating and shoulder carefully skimmed with a graver to run true. The wheel is tapped on and riveted down with suitable punches or a hollow punch. The surplus rivet is then cleaned up with a graver.

Either method will give you a true running wheel, but both need care in execution.

Pinions

Of all the parts of a clock, the pinions seem to cause the most head scratching among those who are considering making their first clock. As with most jobs, however, once you have the correct tools, the job becomes the proverbial piece of cake.

If you have a toolpost or vertical slide milling spindle with suitable drive, or a dividing head to fit on your milling machine, then you already have suitable tools, and you no doubt know how to use them. If you have not, then some more toolmaking is called for, but it will be a relatively quick job - a week of evenings in the workshop will give you a small dividing head for use on the vertical slide.

A small milling spindle with plain bearings, quite suitable for this relatively light duty application, would be even quicker to make, and pinions could then be cut in the same way as wheels. However, this approach has the disadvantage of needing a relatively slow and powerful overhead drive.

I will therefore concentrate on the idea of making a simple dividing head. In conjunction with this, one can mount the cutter in the lathe mandrel, where the power and speed range is more than adequate.

The tool, or tool system, is designed to use a standard ¼" (6 mm.) capacity drill chuck from a "DIY" electric drill. These usually have a male thread for fitting to the drill, which is ideal for our application. A Jacobs chuck is also quite suitable, but you will want one with a male thread on the back end - these are available, but they are more commonly seen with a female thread. Do not get one with a Jacobs taper fitting, because we want to be able to remove and replace the chuck easily from time to time, as you will soon see.

Fig. 33 illustrates the tool. A couple of small division plates will need to be made; one with 24 and 20 divisions will do most jobs, but one with 18 and 14 division will also be useful, as 7-leaf pinions are quite common. If you have a milling machine, you may prefer to use the little dividing fixture on that, but it was designed for use on the vertical slide on the lathe, and I have used mine that way for nearly 20 years.

When making the tool, the female thread for the chuck in both the dividing head mandrel and the Morse taper arbor should be screwcut if possible, rather than tapped. By this means they can be made a very close, even slightly stiff, fit for the chuck, thus ensuring accuracy. Other than that, the making of the equipment shown in Fig. 33 should need little comment.

In use, the chuck is first fitted to the Morse taper arbor; this assembly is secured in the lathe mandrel with a draw bar. A piece of sliver steel of suitable diameter and length for the pinion/arbor is next fitted into the chuck. This workpiece must obviously be long enough to include a chucking portion, the item wanted, plus about 3 - 4 mm. at the outer end to be supported by a tailstock centre, male or female, your choice.

We will typically be making a one piece arbor/pinion, on which the pinion is usually close to one end of the arbor. For maximum rigidity during machining, we want this end nearest the chuck.

Fig 33 : dividing head for cutting pinions.

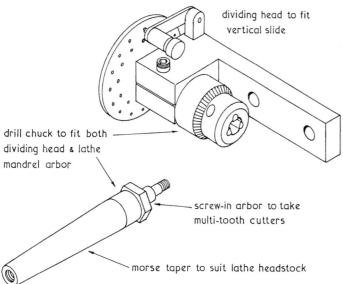

dividing head to fit vertical slide

drill chuck to fit both dividing head & lathe mandrel arbor

screw-in arbor to take multi-tooth cutters

morse taper to suit lathe headstock

Make sure there is enough length for the cutter to run through the pinion without cutting teeth in the chuck as well!

With a tailstock support, turn the workpiece down to the OD of the pinion. (If this OD is larger than the capacity of the chuck, then turn a chucking piece on the material before fitting it into the chuck.) Aim for a good finish at the pinion position. Now turn down the "outer" length of the arbor to about 0.2 mm. over its final diameter. This arbor may well be less than 2 mm. diameter and over 40 mm. long, so take care.

Use a very sharp and pointed tool with plenty of top rake, set dead on centre height. Use a very fine feed, shallow cuts and fairly high spindle speed. Don't worry too much about finish, as it will be cleaned up in the turns or throw later. With a narrow parting tool, take a shallow cut at the "inner" end of the pinion to mark its length. If you don't do this at this stage, you may bend the leaves later, when you try to turn down this end of the arbor, which can lead to much nasty muttering. Just cut in to leave ⅔ to ¾ of the original diameter, so as not to compromise rigidity for cutting the leaves.

Set up the vertical slide facing the headstock, mount the dividing head on the vertical slide, and transfer the chuck-plus-workpiece to the dividing head.

A small screw-in arbor, with the appropriate multi-tooth pinion cutter attached, is then fitted to the Morse taper plug still fitted in the headstock mandrel.

The axis of the workpiece is then oriented across the lathe with the "outer" end facing the operator. The workpiece, which should be below the cutter, is fed out towards the operator (and the cutter) via the cross slide feed crank.

This puts the cut on top of the work, where it is clearly visible. Also, the cutter is trying to push the job into the dividing head/chuck, rather than pull it out. Take great care to ensure that the axis of the workpiece is exactly centred under the cutter. If you are off only a couple of thou, the job is a scrap, as you will have wolves' teeth again.

Using the vertical slide, feed the workpiece up to the cutter until it is just touching, and take a "cut" the length of the pinion. This will immediately show whether or not the dividing head is set truly parallel with the surface of the lathe bed. If it is satisfactory, lock all slides not being used, including the saddle, feed the work up to the cutter and take a cut of about ⅓ tooth depth.

Index around, cutting the required number of teeth to this depth. Make another trip around for the second ⅓ of tooth depth. Then start feeding the vertical slide up slowly, and alternately cut two adjacent teeth until you are cutting full depth, or perhaps a thou less, then cut the remainder of the teeth with one pass each.

Go around once more at the same setting to remove that last thou and clean up.

A pinion of 0.6 or 0.7 module can be cut easily in three passes as detailed above without any support under the work, as the forces trying to deflect the work are quite small if the cutter is sharp. For modules of 0.8 to 1.0, I would prefer four, or possibly five, passes, with a final skim to clean up some of the tool marks.

The chuck is then returned to the Morse arbor in the lathe for turning the "inner" end of the arbor to size. This is a tricky job, and must not be hurried. Use a narrow parting tool, very sharp, and with plenty of top rake. Support the outer end of the work with the tailstock centre. Start by widening the cut you have already made by cutting in a little nearer the headstock, and go very slowly to full depth. Now work towards the face of the pinion and take very shallow and slow cuts until you have cleaned it up. Go very carefully, as there is a real risk of bending the leaves.

Take successive cuts towards the headstock to widen the gap. Go slowly and take shallow cuts; there will be a lot of "rattle" until you have cleaned up the runout of the pinion cutter. After this you can safely take heavier cuts until you have the length and diameter you require.

The pinion leaves must next be polished. It is convenient to do this while the workpiece is still in the chuck. Remove the chuck/Morse arbor from the lathe - you will find that the arbor is a convenient handle for holding the work. We now need two discs of hardboard about 50 mm. diameter x 3 mm. thick. Turn them up with a suitable centre hole to fit another of the little screw-in stub arbors that you have made for wheels and cutters, and label one disc "grinding" and the other "polishing".

Now you see why it is so very useful to have two of

these Morse taper arbors in your tool kit: it extends the capability of the system, particularly in view of the fact that drill chucks, stub arbors and dividing head are all interchangeable.

If you don't have a second Morse arbor at this stage, then grip the stub arbor by its spanner hexagon in the 3-jaw - it will serve for the moment.

Fit your grinding disc to the stub arbor in the lathe. Run it at about 300 rpm, and present the pinion to the bottom edge of the disc, i.e. so the edge is running *away* from you. Now let the face of the pinion cut a profile in the edge of the disc until the disc will fit neatly between two pinion leaves, right down to the root diameter of the pinion. Hold the pinion/chuck assembly very firmly, so that the disc cannot snatch it away from you.

Now load the spaces between the pinion leaves with fine grinding paste, and again present the job to the edge of the rotating disc. Moving the pinion backwards and forwards, you can very quickly grind out all tool marks. Fig. 34 illustrates the method.

Only a few strokes are required between each pair of leaves, as the disc quickly becomes impregnated with grinding paste.

After washing the pinion in a solvent such as white spirit to remove all traces of grinding paste, it is loaded with a polishing medium, and the same procedure followed again, using the other of the two hardboard discs. You will need only a few strokes on the periphery of the disc to bring the leaves of the pinion to a high finish.

The best material I have yet found for polishing is "Solvol Autosol". This is sold for use mainly in the motor industry, and is readily available from motorists' suppliers, garages etc. It is a paste in a tube, and therefore much more manageable than a liquid polish.

The pinion can be cut from the chucking piece and set up in the throw to finish the arbor and turn the pivots. Cut it off perhaps 1.5 mm. over length, as you will need to put a centre in

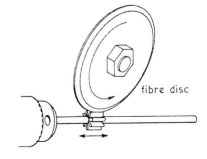

Fig 34 : pinion polishing.

fibre disc

the end. (There's already a centre in the other end, if you've been following instructions!) Take a skim over the length of the arbor with a graver, to bring it to the required diameter and leave a nice finish. Polish the arbor with emery sticks. Also polish both end faces of the pinion to leave a nice finish here, and to remove any burrs on the end of the pinion leaves.

Finally, turn the pivots, cut to length, round off the ends and polish and burnish as already described. Small pinions are delicate things to make, but if carefully made and nicely finished and polished, they enhance the appearance of the finished clock and - more importantly - they work more efficiently.

The foregoing has dealt with small pinions which, because of their size, have to be made integral with the arbor. Larger pinions, either of a higher count or a larger module, can often be made separately from their arbor, and fixed to it in a manner similar to that used to fix wheel collets. This simplifies the job somewhat, as the arbor can be made from a stock size material, and the pinion head drilled to suit.

If you take this approach, the pinion material still needs to be long enough to include a chucking piece, and having turned the OD, the centre hole is drilled before transferring to the dividing head for the leaves to be cut. The pinion head can then be cut from the chucking piece with a junior hacksaw, after

which the sawn end must be cleaned up in the lathe. The best method of doing this is by holding it in a one-off female arbor. This prevents distorting the pinion leaves as the chuck jaws might.

Chuck a piece of brass bar about 10 to 12 mm. long in the 3-jaw, and drill and bore through until the pinion head will not quite enter. Then enlarge the hole with a taper broach until the pinion head will enter about 1.5 mm. or a little more, and then tap it in another 3 mm. or so, so that it is securely held. The sawn face can then be cleaned up with a very sharp tool with plenty of top rake. Once again, take very fine cuts, to avoid bending the leaves.

The pinion head can be polished before it is removed from the chuck, as already described, or after it is fixed to its arbor. The latter course is probably the best, as the grinding paste will also remove the minute burrs raised by the last facing cut on the sawn end. A useful tool for holding the arbor for this final job is an old drill chuck fixed to a large file handle. This is also very useful for holding needle files, broaches, and other small round pieces while they are being worked on.

Having now got a wheel on one arbor and a pinion on another, they must be "depthed" for correct meshing. The theoretical centre-to-centre distance for the two arbors is the sum of the two PCDs divided by 2. An engineer would accept this figure without question, and then proceed to "run it in" until all worked freely! However, there can be no "running in period" with a clock - everything must work freely (but not sloppily) from the start, or the clock simply will not function.

The wheels and pinions are depthed and checked for free running by setting them up in an adjustable depthing tool. This same tool is then used to mark the centre distances on the clock plate, or as clockmakers say, "plant the train".

Fig. 35 shows a traditional clockmaker's depthing tool. They can be purchased, but are expensive, although at the time of writing, a kit from which the buyer can make his

Fig 35: traditional clockmaker's depthing tool.

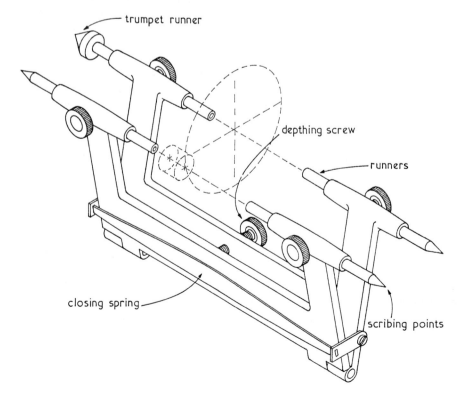

own is available from JMW Clocks - see Appendix III. It is well within the capabilities of a competent model engineer to make one, and would be worth the time spent doing so.

If you do decide to make one, the main point to bear in mind is that the centre lines of the bottom hinge and the two pairs of runners must all be exactly parallel.

The appearance of the tool suggests its use. The wheel on its arbor is held between the female centres of one pair of runners, and the pinion between the other pair. The centre distance of the runners can then be fine adjusted with the depth adjusting screw until the wheel and pinion mesh freely. The tool, with the wheel and pinion still in place, is then taken to the clock plate and used like a pair of dividers to mark out or "plant" the required centres for that wheel and pinion pair.

A few words on what is meant by "free meshing" may be appropriate.

Cycloidal gears are designed to work "after the line of centres". This line of centres is a straight line between the centres of the meshing wheel and pinion. If the driving tooth meets the driven tooth before this line, the two teeth are trying to push into each other, and push the two wheels apart, thus causing friction and wear. The two teeth should not make contact until they reach the line of centres and are momentarily moving parallel to each other. Beyond this point the paths of the two contacting teeth start to diverge, and the driving tooth is pushing the driven tooth away from it, causing much less friction.

In theory, the two teeth roll off each other with no friction at all, gradually parting company as the next pair of teeth reach the line of centres and make gentle contact. This also is an important point, that the diverging teeth do not lose contact until the following pair have made contact - there must be no "drop" or free play as the converging teeth meet.

In practice, with the use of the depthing tool, all this is quite easy to achieve. One simply puts the wheel and pinion in the tool and adjusts until they mesh. Apply slight finger pressure to produce some drag against the pinion arbor, and then spin the wheel. You will probably hear quite a rattle as the teeth engage. Use the depthing screw to adjust the meshing finely until there is as little noise as possible when you spin the wheel. You will probably not eliminate noise altogether, as nothing is ever 100% perfect, but the quietest setting will be the point of minimum friction.

If you then inspect the mesh with an eyeglass, you should find that the contact is on the line of centres, and the teeth come into contact with no drop. The centre-to-centre distance which provides this happy state of affairs is then marked on the plates with the scribing points of the depthing tool runners. When doing this, make sure the tool is truly perpendicular to the plate, otherwise your marked centres will not be accurate. You may need to adjust the extension of one of the runners to achieve this.

For unmounted wheels and pinion heads, a much easier-to-make form of depthing tool can be used. This type is detailed in the chapter on escapements, as its prime purpose is the marking out and shaping of escapement pallets.

Escapements

By far the most common escapement used by amateur clockmakers is the recoil, or "anchor", escapement. Many other escapements have recoil action, but this is the one generally known by that name. In pendulum clocks it is the most common escapement of all, and is the one that we will deal with in detail. All the common escapements contain built-in timekeeping errors, and the recoil type is no exception. However, within limits, its errors are largely cancelled out by the fundamental error of the pendulum, i.e. the pendulum is not isochronous if its amplitude of swing varies. (Admittedly that statement needs qualification, but we can accept it as effectively true for all domestic clocks.)

An escapement has to do two things:

1. Supply a regular impulse to the pendulum to keep it swinging, and:

2. Count the swings of the pendulum in order that the clock shows the correct time (assuming that the pendulum length and overall gear train ratio are properly related to each other in the first place).

Fig. 36 shows the layout of the recoil escapement, such as one might find in a typical longcase clock. The following will explain its workings briefly.

The escape wheel has 30 teeth, and we shall assume that it is driving a one second pendulum; the movement thus indicates seconds on the dial. The pallets span a quarter of these teeth, i.e. 7½ teeth,

Fig 36 : <u>the recoil escapement</u> .

entry pallet   exit pallet

hence this is referred to as a "square" escapement layout; more of this in a moment. In Fig. 36 the escapement is shown as seen from the front of the clock, and the escape wheel revolves clockwise.

The pendulum (indicated only by a dashed line in Fig. 36) is swinging to the right and is about 2° past the midpoint of its swing. The exit pallet has just released a tooth, and the corresponding tooth under the entry pallet has just landed on the pallet's face. At this point the pendulum continues to swing to the right, pushing the entry pallet deeper into the teeth of the escape wheel. As it does so, it pushes the wheel back, or anti-clockwise. This is the recoil part of the action, from which this type of escapement takes its name. The pendulum then reaches the end of its swing and starts to return, swinging to the left.

The entry pallet begins moving out of engagement with the teeth of the escape wheel, and in fact it is the power of the weight or spring driving the escape wheel that is actually pushing the pallet away as the tooth slides along the face of the pallet, with the wheel now turning clockwise. This push from the clock's motive power is known as impulse, as the tooth, via the pallet, is at this moment transmitting the impulse that actually drives the pendulum.

When the tooth reaches the tip of the pallet, it escapes, and the wheel is free of restraint, but by now the pendulum is about 2° to the left of its mid-

point, and the exit pallet has descended between the seventh and eighth teeth, counting from the one that just left the entry pallet. The seventh tooth therefore lands on the exit pallet face and stops. The short free movement of the escape wheel before it is stopped by the exit (or entry) pallet is known as *drop*.

Drop should be kept to a minimum, as it represents wasted energy. In a well made escapement, it will probably be no more than 1° of movement of the escape wheel.

The pendulum is still swinging to the left, and the exit pallet now performs exactly as the entry pallet did on the last "tick" - that is to say, recoil, impulse, and drop, after which we are back in exactly the same position as shown in Fig. 36, except that the escape wheel has moved clockwise the distance of one complete tooth space, the clock has ticked twice, and two seconds of time have passed.

It is worth stressing that the recoil action is very important, as without it the clock will soon stop. Typically the total recoil arc (i.e. both sides added together) is equal to the impulse arc. In the above explanation I have assumed that the pendulum swings a total of 4° between drops. Therefore the total arc of the pendulum, including recoil action, should be about 8°, giving 2° of recoil each side.

From the foregoing, and from studying the diagram, you will see that the escape wheel only moves half a tooth for each "tick" or each beat of the pendulum. Thus a one second pendulum needs an escape wheel of only 30 teeth to indicate seconds on the dial, the wheel revolving once a minute.

Fig 37 : <u>elevation & part section :</u>
<u>escapement & pendulum suspension</u> .

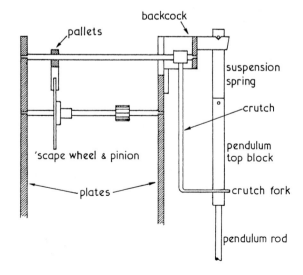

Fig 38

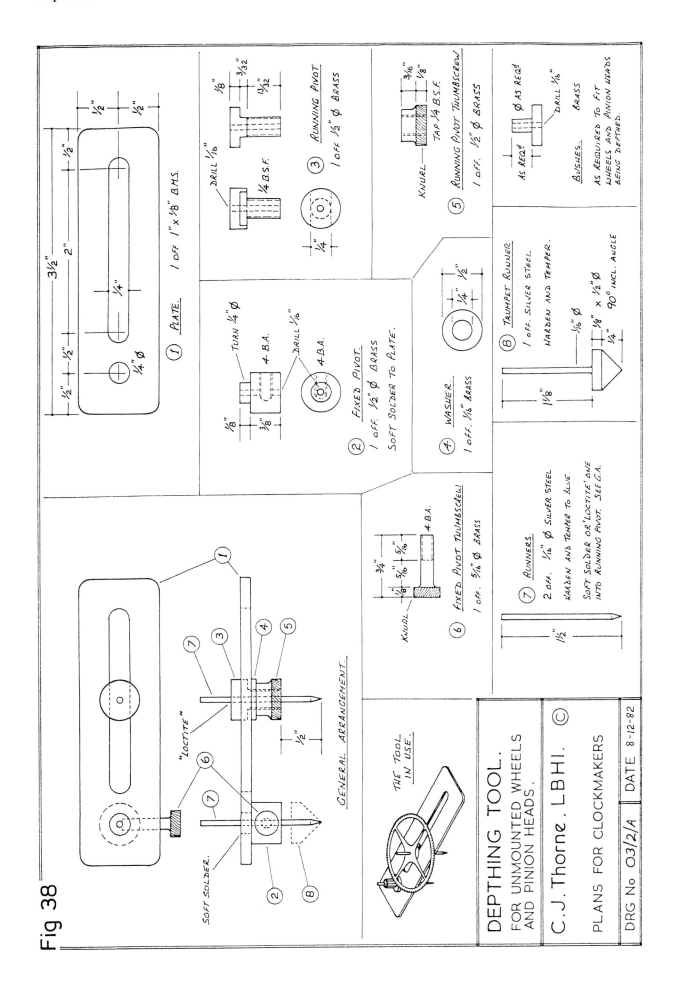

In clockmaker's terms, the beat of a pendulum is the time taken for it to swing from one extremity to the other, or - if you like - from "tick" to "tock". A one second pendulum - sometimes called a seconds beating pendulum - is approximately 994 mm. long. A theorist would say that this is a two-second pendulum, as he takes each beat (which he calls a "period") to be a complete oscillation from rest position (straight down) to maximum swing to one side, through to maximum swing the other side, and back to the rest point. Clockmakers, on the other hand, take the view that since the escape wheel moves each time the pendulum reverses direction, the event to be considered is the pendulum's swing in one direction or the other.

The impulse is imparted to the pendulum from the pallets via the crutch. Fig. 37 shows the

arrangement, and this will be discussed in detail in the chapter on pendulums.

However, we will now consider the details of making a set of pallets.

The first requirement for making recoil pallets is the small depthing tool shown in Fig. 38. This drawing is an early version of one of my "Plans for Clockmakers" series, and has since been redrawn with metric dimensions. None of the measurements are critical, as long as the tool is well made. The runners are shown as being 1.6 mm. diameter, but they could with advantage be slightly larger, say 2 mm. The tool is shown being used for depthing unmounted wheels and pinions, but it is for making pallets that it is most useful, if not essential. The original design of this device is not mine. It was described by F.J. Britten at the end of the 19th century, and I doubt that it was a new idea then.

W.J. Gazeley was the first to describe in print the following method of laying out pallets (albeit using a piece of paper, rather than the actual pallet material). The method to be described is therefore popularly known as the Gazeley Method. However, Gazeley showed only, as an example, an escape wheel of 30 teeth, but the method is universal, and can be used for any escape wheel tooth count and/or pallet span, as will be demonstrated. It is an entirely practical method, and full control can be exercised throughout the operation.

For the purpose of illustration, I will use as an example an escape wheel of 30 teeth, and pallets that are required to span 7½ teeth, i.e. one quarter of the number of teeth in the wheel. This ratio is fairly standard with the recoil escapement and, as already noted, is known as a "square" layout. Note that pallets always span some number of whole teeth plus half a tooth. The reason for this will become obvious as we proceed.

Refer next to Fig. 39, Diagram 1. First set the pivots of the depthing tool the same distance apart as the theoretical distance between the escape wheel arbor and the pallet arbor. In a square layout this is always 1.41 x escape wheel radius. Precisely why this is so I will explain a little later.

Fig 39 : marking out recoil pallets.

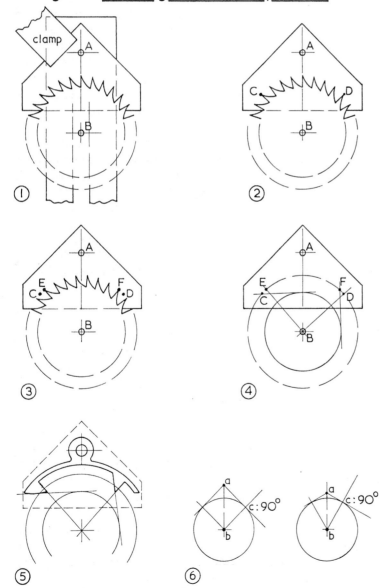

Cut a piece of gauge plate roughly triangular, and large enough to contain the finished pallets. In it, drill a hole to fit the runner of the depthing tool's fixed pivot. Coat the gauge plate with layout blue, and clamp the blank to the tool. On the pallet blank, scribe a vertical line A-B that passes through the centres of the runners. Your wheel will probably have a centre hole much larger than the depthing tool runners, so turn up a shouldered bush to carry the wheel on the runner in the running pivot, which runs in the slot in the depthing tool.

Now refer to Fig. 39, Diagram 2. Line up one tooth of the escape wheel with the centre line A-B. Now count over to the fourth tooth either side of the centre line, and make a small dot on the pallet blank at the tip of each of these teeth to mark points C and D. Next, move the escape wheel so that the centre line falls exactly halfway between two teeth, as in Diagram 3. Again count over to the fourth tooth either side of the centre line, and mark points E and F at their tips.

Now remove the escape wheel from the tool, and in its place put either a piece of card on which is drawn a circle with a diameter equal to 0.7 of that of the escape wheel, or a turned disc of any suitable material and of the same reduced diameter. This puts us at Diagram 4 in Fig. 39.

On the pallet blank, scribe the two radial lines passing through points D and E to the escape wheel centre. Also scribe two lines at a tangent to the reduced diameter circle, one to pass through point C and the other to pass through point F.

This modest amount of effort has given us the necessary lines for the pallet nibs. All the remaining lines to be scribed are really cosmetic, to give a pleasing overall shape to the piece. Fig. 39, Diagram 5, shows a typical example. The "tail" to the right of the exit pallet is purely cosmetic, and gives balance to the shape, otherwise the pallets tend to look a little lopsided, although they will function just as efficiently.

The only other point to bear in mind is that the pallet nibs need to be about 1½ times the depth of the escape wheel teeth.

The pallet blank can now be removed from the depthing tool, and carefully cut and filed to the scribed lines. Don't worry about final finish yet, as there is more work to be done. Fit the pallets and wheel back in the depth tool and try rocking the pallets to let the wheel pass. Observe carefully what happens. There is no clearance, and the wheel will

not turn. This is where we need to make haste slowly. Carefully file a small and equal amount of the back faces (lines D-B and E-B) of the pallets and try the wheel again. Most likely you will not have removed enough, and the wheel will still not pass. Repeat this process until one or the other of the pallets will just let a tooth pass and then concentrate on the other pallet.

It is important that you do not remove too much or one pallet will have a larger "drop" than the other. Both drops should be equal, and as small as possible compatible with free action.

DO NOT remove any more metal from the impulse face of the pallets (the tangent lines)! When both pallets are just - and only just - allowing the wheel teeth to pass, use emery paper to give a fine finish to the whole piece. On the pallet faces, this will remove just enough metal to give a reliable working clearance.

It is advantageous to put a slight convex curve on the impulse face of the entry pallet. This eases recoil stresses, but be careful to work away from the tip of the pallet. Any more metal removed here would shorten the back face of the pallet, increase the drop to the exit pallet and decrease the impulse angle of the entry pallet that you are working on.

The whole pallet piece (or *anchor* as it is commonly called) should now have a fine emery finish all over. The nibs must now be hardened by heating to cherry red, holding at that temperature for a few moments, and then quenching in oil. Harden just the pallet nibs, not the whole piece. Do them one at a time, and be careful not to draw the temper of the first one when doing the second - hold them in a large pair of pliers to form a heat sink just behind the pallet you are heating. Do not temper - leave them glass hard.

It would be a good idea to add a couple of little slabs of aluminium sheet between the plier jaws and the pallet, both the protect the polish on the metal and as a further heat sink, aluminium being a very good conductor of heat.

The whole piece can then be polished with fine emery paper. The impulse faces of the two pallets can be polished with a piece of wood impregnated with Solvol Autosol or similar polishing paste. We want a mirror finish on these faces.

I will stress again that when fitting pallets, aim for the minimum amount of drop compatible with reliable clearance. Excess drop is wasted energy, and if it is wasted, it will not be there to give impulse. If you find that you have taken too much off the back face of either, or both, of the pallets, the only thing to do is scrap the piece and start again. Do not try bending the pallet arms to correct any error, as this upsets the whole geometry of the layout and creates more problems than it solves.

The last job to do is to use the depthing tool to mark the position of the pallet arbor on the plates, and to drill and broach the holes to fit the pivots.

In the foregoing paragraphs I have detailed how to mark out the pallets that are to span 7½ teeth of a 30 tooth escape wheel, but the "Gazeley" method can obviously be used for a wheel of any tooth count, and for pallets to span any required number of teeth.

You will have noticed that to mark points C,D,E and F in Fig. 39, we counted four teeth either side of the centre line. In other words, we counted half the number of the next even number above the number of teeth to be spanned by the pallets. This is always the case where the pallets span an odd number of teeth. For example, if the pallets must span 9½ teeth, the next even number is 10, therefore we would count five teeth either side of the centre line. This is not influenced by the total number of teeth in the escape wheel.

If the pallets must span an even number of teeth, it is slightly more complicated. Say the pallets must span 8½ teeth: we would then count half that number (four, ignoring the half tooth), when marking as in Diagram 2, but we would count four plus one - five - when marking as in Diagram 3, where the centre line falls between two teeth. When you do this, you will notice that Diagram 2 actually marks point E and F and Diagram 3 marks points C and D, the reverse of that shown in Fig. 39. This is correct, and you now have the four dots required to mark out the pallets as in Diagram 4, using the same impulse face circle of 0.7 x escape wheel diameter as described earlier, and from which the tangent lines are taken to mark the impulse faces of the pallets.

You may ask the significance of the impulse face being 0.7 of the radius of the escape wheel. To be more precise, it should be 0.707, which is the cosine of 45°, but in practical terms 0.7 is accurate enough. It ensures that the impulse faces of the pallets are at 45° to the tangent of the escape wheel; a moment's thought will show that because the pallets have to give recoil as well as take impulse, this is the optimum angle. The impulse faces will also be at 45° to the tangent of the arc described by the pallets, and thus we are as near as we can get to an ideal situation.

I will now explain, as promised, the other little bit of theory concerning the centre-to-centre distance between escape wheel and pallet arbors. We have already said that in a square layout (see Fig. 39, Diagram 6) this distance is 1.41 times the radius of the escape wheel.

Where does this number 1.41 come from?

1.41 is the secant (the reciprocal of the cosine) of 45°, which is the angle at the centre of the escape wheel, defined by the points a, b and c.

If we wish the pallets to span fewer teeth, say ⅙ instead of ¼ of the escape wheel diameter, then the layout will be somewhat less than "square", and the angle abc will be 30°, as in the right hand example in Diagram 6, Fig. 39. The secant of 30° is 1.155, which is therefore the factor by which to multiply the escape wheel radius to obtain centre distance in this case.

In practice, this is a poor example, as the pallet arbor is too close to the escape wheel teeth for comfort. Pallets which span such a small proportion of the escape wheel teeth are not recommended. Manufacturers of mass produced clocks have done this in the past, and they got around the problem by planting the pallet arbor further away from the escape wheel than theory dictates. This can lead to problems, particularly with the entry pallet. What happens is that if the pallet angle is "right" for impulse, it is too "flat" for efficient recoil and vice versa. This can lead to rapid wear of both the pallets and the escape wheel pivots.

It is quite feasible to go the other way, and have the pallets spanning more than a quarter of the teeth - in fact they can happily span up to two fifths. This actually reduces the arc of the pendulum, and can lead to better timekeeping. (The shorter pallet span discussed in the previous paragraph has the reverse effect.) To give an example of the effect this has on arbor centre spacing, consider an escape wheel of 36 teeth, with the pallets spanning 12½ teeth. 12½ teeth represent 125°, so the angle abc in Diagram 6 would then be 62.5°. The secant of this angle is 2.166, and with a 40 mm. diameter escape wheel, the arbor centres would be 43.3 mm. apart. (2.166 x escape wheel radius of 20 mm. = 43.3 mm.) This would be quite a good layout for a precision timekeeper with a dead beat escapement. However, we are really only concerned here with domestic timekeepers, and over the last 300 years or so, the recoil escapement with the traditional square layout has proved to be the most reliable for this purpose.

At the risk of repeating a point made several pages back, I will say one final word on the functioning of recoil escapement: there must be sufficient power at the escape wheel to give a healthy recoil. If the escape wheel does not recoil, the clock will soon stop for lack of impulse.

Two other escapements are often used by amateur clockmakers. These are the *dead beat* and the *verge*. They are illustrated in Fig. 40. I do not propose to deal with them in detail, as I do not consider either of them really suitable for someone building their first clock.

The *dead beat* is similar in many ways to the recoil escapement. It was developed from the latter type, but it does not recoil, hence its name. At the drop, the tooth lands on a pallet face which is actually the circumference of a circle centred on the pallet arbor, so that although the pallet continues to swing on after the drop, before reversing direction, the escape wheel remains stationary. It is known as a frictional rest escapement, and when well made provides very good timekeeping, particularly when used in conjunction with a temperature compensated pendulum. It is much used in regulators and other high grade timekeepers. Its proportions can be quite

Fig 40 : Deadbeat & Verge escapements.

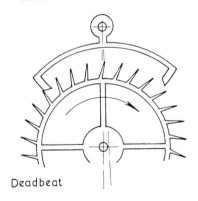
Deadbeat

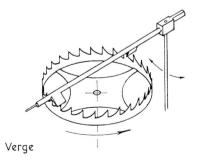
Verge

critical, so if you wish to use it, you will need to read up on it first.

The other popular escapement is the *verge*. It has been used for over 700 years, first with a device known as a foliot, then with a balance wheel, and finally with a pendulum. Indeed, it was the escapement used with the first successful pendulum clocks, in 1657. It too is a recoil escapement, and needs very careful fitting into the clock. If not set up correctly in the first place, it will be out of beat and the only thing to do will be to start again. Today it is used only in "reproduction" work, as it is not a very good timekeeper, and needs more power to drive it than the normal recoil escapement. It also needs a contrate wheel in the train, as the escape wheel turns on a vertical axis when driving a pendulum.

Pendulums

This book is concerned only with pendulum regulated clocks, for two reasons. Firstly, it is the easiest type of clock to build from scratch, hence is the type the amateur clockmaker is most likely to build, certainly for a first clock. Secondly, the pendulum seems to have a fascination that other oscillators, such as the balance wheel, do not possess. After more than 300 years, highly experienced clockmakers are still trying to create the perfect pendulum clock, even though it can offer no advances in terms of the future of accurate timekeeping.

A knowledgeable and experienced amateur can design and make a pendulum regulator clock to match the quartz crystal watch for accuracy. Making a regulator that will beat the caesium atom clock is a different matter - you can't. However, for the moment we are only concerned with making an attractive domestic clock, wherein a performance of plus or minus a minute or two a week is both quite acceptable and easily attained. We will not digress into temperature compensation, circular error, different types of suspension, the aerodynamics of the bob, etc., whereby an accuracy of a second or two a month may be attained.

A basic pendulum consists of a suspension spring, a rod and a bob, along with a means of adjusting the height of the bob for the purpose of regulating the "beat" of the pendulum. It is impulsed from the pallets via the crutch. Fig. 41 illustrates two basic types of pendulum rod, one normally used in longcase clocks, the other more commonly used for bracket and skeleton clocks. As can be seen, the crutch can terminate in either a fork or a pin, depending on the type of rod. Whichever type is

Fig 41 : <u>pendulum rods</u>.

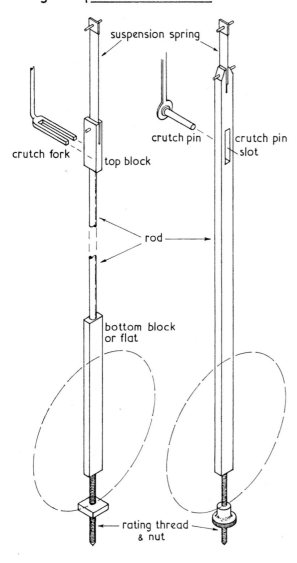

suspension spring

crutch pin

crutch pin slot

crutch fork

top block

rod

bottom block or flat

rating thread & nut

The suspension spring is a short piece of spring steel strip, typically about 5 mm. wide, and from 0.04 mm. to 0.1 mm. thick, depending on its duty. They can be purchased ready-made very cheaply, and you may therefore not care to make your own, unless you want the satisfaction derived from making them yourself. Spring steel strip or sheet can be purchased from horological suppliers for this purpose - Feeler gauge stock is also suitable.

A completed suspension spring will have brass cheeks at the top end, and usually - but not always - on the bottom end also.

To make a suspension spring, cut a suitable length of steel strip, and where the cheeks will be fitted, tin the end with soft solder. Cut a couple of pieces of brass sheet of about 0.4 mm. thickness, and each big enough so that when folded over, like a book, they will form the cheeks. Tin the pieces before folding, and then fold with the tinned face inside. Slip one piece over each end of the steel strip,and sweat in place under pressure to ensure a complete bond. Have the folds along the ends of the strip; the sides can then be trimmed to the same width as the spring.

Drill each piece through for a couple of very small brass rivets (taper pins can be used); rivet flush and file smooth. The spring steel can be drilled easily, at low speed, using a sharp drill.

I would recommend that you use a hand drill, as even the lowest spindle speed on a drill press is likely to be much too high. You need no more than 100 rpm, and plenty of pressure to ensure the drill is going to *cut*, and not *rub*. The hand drill enables you to start very slowly, to prevent the drill from wandering, and also gives you a degree of "feel" as the drill breaks through the material, thus avoiding a snatch.

Sweating plus rivets might seem like overkill for such a small piece, but these springs work hard for their living, and if they break, you will be doing more than a minor repair job on your carefully built clock.

Fig 42 : <u>backcocks</u>.

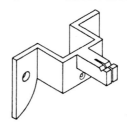

used, there must be as little play as possible between the crutch and the rod, as this is another source of lost energy. On the other hand, there must be complete freedom, with no snagging or stiffness. As you will by now have gathered, this compromise between complete freedom and lack of play is of the essence of clockmaking.

The pendulum is suspended from the backcock, of which two examples are shown in Fig. 42. The one on the left incorporates the back pivot hole for the pallet arbor, and is typical of longcase clocks. The smaller one on the right is purely a pendulum suspension, the pivot hole for the pallet arbor being in the clock's back plate, with a large hole below for the crutch to work through, the crutch obviously being "joggled" to pass through the plate. In a skeleton clock there is clearly no problem in providing this hole!

Finally, drill through the centre of each cheek and fit a taper pin in the top end. The hole on the bottom end is for a pin through the top of the pendulum rod, and said pin must be a free fit in this hole. The pin through the top cheek rests in the vee on the top of the backcock, to take the weight of the pendulum. Some clocks - longcase clocks in particular - do not have this pin fitted. In these, the slot in the backcock is made just wide enough to receive the spring, and the cheeks, resting on the top of the cock, take the weight of the pendulum. In this case, the dual security of both rivetting and sweating of the cheeks to the spring is particularly necessary.

It is important that the spring is not tight in the slot in either the backcock or the pendulum rod, to ensure that, when installed, the pendulum hangs truly vertical. If it does not, the bob will "roll" when swinging. On the other hand - and you have read this before - the fit must not be sloppy.

The pendulum rod can be a single piece, as in a bracket or skeleton clock, or built up, as is common in longcase clocks. The one-piece pendulum is usually made of brass, although that is not a good material because of its high coefficient of expansion, which adversely affects timekeeping. Steel would be a better material, but does not look as attractive in a skeleton clock or bracket clock with a glass panel case.

The best material for pendulum rods is Invar, a term you may have heard before. "Invar" (from the word 'invariable') is a steel alloy with an extremely low coefficient of expansion. However, it is not an easy material to work, and its use in a domestic timekeeper such as we are considering here is not justified, as it will not significantly improve the clock's overall timekeeping ability. Plan to put an Invar rod in your first fine Regulator clock, where it is fully justified. Most clockmakers' material supply houses can supply Invar rod for a seconds pendulum already cut to length and threaded at both ends to receive the top block and the rating nut.

It may surprise you to learn that wood also makes a good Regulator pendulum rod, although it will not be quite as good as a rod made from Invar steel.

The rating thread can be a separate piece screwed into the bottom end of the rod and secured with adhesive or soft solder, or it can be cut on the end of the rod, making a one-piece unit.

The built-up rod consists of a top block, a rod and a bottom block, sometimes called the "flat". The two blocks are usually made of brass, while the rod is of

An 8 day table or bracket timepiece in an "architectural" style case, based on a clock by AHASUERUS FROMANTEEL of London (late of Holland and an associate and friend of Salomon Coster). This clock has a verge escapement and a false pendulum showing through a cut-out in the dial.

steel. Both blocks are screwed onto the rod; they may be simply screwed in tight, or secured with soft solder or adhesive if desired. Again, the rating thread below the bottom block can be either a separate piece screwed in, or it may be screwcut on the end of the flat material, after turning to size.

The rating nut is usually made from brass. If it will not be seen in the finished clock, say a longcase, it need be nothing fancier than a square nut about 12 mm. across the flats. A square nut is easier to regulate the clock with, as it is easy to see how far you have turned it. In a skeleton clock the nut is usually a fancy piece of turning, with the largest diameter knurled, the appearance of the piece being more important than practical considerations would demand.

Pendulum bobs on mass produced clocks are often castings of iron or lead. The standard longcase bob over the centuries has been made thus, often with a brass face on one side. However, we will want something a little more attractive.

The bob can be a cylindrical piece of polished brass or steel, in which case drill a hole through the centre to take a round rod, no flat being fitted, and the bottom of the rod threaded for the rating nut. The hole through the bob could also be partially threaded for rating and the rating nut used as a locknut.

Fig 43 : <u>pendulum bob.</u>

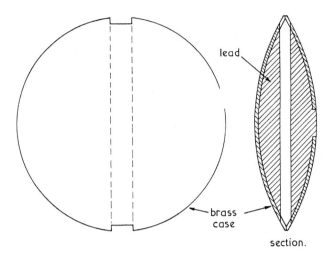

lead

brass
case

section.

The classic, or most common bob, is of lenticular shape, and is made from two brass shells soldered together face to face at their edges, and filled with lead.

Fig. 43 shows a bob of this type. The two shells are formed by spinning, and the finished bob is filled with molten lead poured in through a hole in the centre of the rear shell.

As you may not have done any metal spinning, I will describe the process in some detail. The type of brass can affect the ease with which the job can be done. I find that clockmakers' brass does not spin very well

- even when annealed it seems to remain a little springy. The normal "half hard" brass sheet seems to spin quite well, and the act of spinning burnishes it to a nice finish, but it can be variable: some pieces need much more annealing than others. Soft brass sheet will spin quite well, and you won't need to anneal for the first spin, but it does not finish as well, and will need more polishing. If your material dealer sells a brass sheet which is known to be suitable for spinning, they you are all set. Otherwise, you will have to take a little pot luck.

For the simple shapes we wish to spin, the tools required are easily made. They consist of a pressure pad for the tailstock, a fulcrum pin for the tool rest, and the spinning tool itself. Fig. 44 shows all of these items, plus the necessary wood former to put in the 3-jaw, and against which to spin the bob shells.

The spinning tool is made from a piece of 10 mm. diameter silver steel rod about 250 mm. or 300 mm. long. Turn one end to an elongated but blunt bullet nose shape; this task can be done freehand in the lathe with a file. File a flat about 25 mm. long at such an angle that it finishes about 2 mm. short of the tip, rounding off the sharp edges and in fact leaving the flat slightly convex. Polish this working end, harden and temper, and then polish again.

Fit a large wooden file handle onto the other end of the tool. Make sure it is a secure fit, or epoxy it in place, for it must not move when being used.

Fig 44 : <u>spinning.</u>

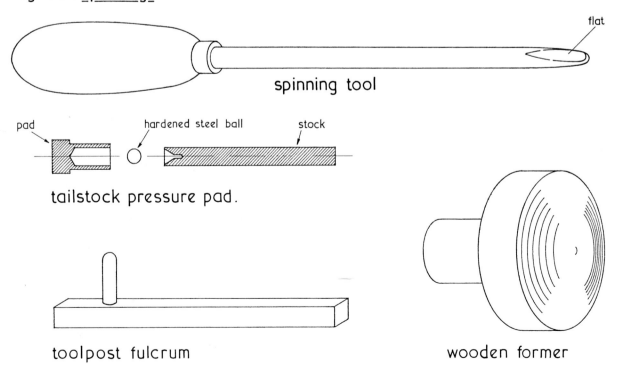

flat

spinning tool

pad   hardened steel ball   stock

tailstock pressure pad.

toolpost fulcrum   wooden former

A professional metal spinner will have a range of tools with different shaped ends, but this one tool will spin all the pendulum shells we are ever likely to want, plus the odd bell or two.

The toolpost fulcrum consists of a piece of 12 mm. square mild steel about 120 mm. long, with a pin of about 6 mm. diameter threaded and screwed into one face about 25 mm. from one end. The pin should stand up about 25 mm. The bar is clamped in the toolpost parallel with the lathe bed, and the pin serves as a fixed point around which to lever the spinning tool. On the short end of the square bar, beyond the pin, it is not a bad idea to round off the top face slightly.

The pressure pad, which is in fact a rather simple live or running centre with a flat face, is clamped in the tailstock chuck. To make this item, first centre drill the stock, which can be a piece of mild steel bar about 6 to 8 mm. diameter. The pad is then drilled and bored to a nice running fit over the stock. The ball should have plenty of grease on it before assembly, and should be kept well greased. There is no need to harden the stock or the pad, the face of which should be about 12 mm. diameter for our purpose.

The wood former is simply a piece of thick ply or board cut roughly to the desired diameter and bored part way through to accept a piece of dowel about 25 mm. diameter, glued in, for a chucking piece. The former is then turned to the same OD as the proposed bob, and domed to match the desired profile of the shells that will be spun against it.

Before starting work on the bob, turn up a second pressure pad to fit the stock, but this time with a shallow spigot in the centre the same size as the hole we will need in the centre of one of the shells. This will locate that shell on the former.

For purposes of illustration I will assume you wish to spin a bob of about 70 mm. diameter. For an elegant shape, the thickness of the bob in the centre should be between $\frac{1}{5}$ and $\frac{1}{6}$ of its diameter, say 12 mm. Therefore our wooden former should be domed about 6 mm. This can be roughly profiled with a suitable lathe tool in the toolpost, and then finished freehand with a file. To help grip the workpiece, use double sided sticky tape to attach a piece of coarse emery paper, face outwards, in the centre of the former.

Cut two discs of 0.8 mm. or 1 mm. brass just over 70 mm. diameter, and drill a hole of about 7 or 8 mm. diameter in the centre of one piece. There is no need to turn the OD of these pieces yet - just saw to the scribed circle and file off the burrs.

Anneal both pieces by heating to red and then either allowing to cool naturally or by quenching in water - it makes no difference to brass.

Set the wooden former in the 3-jaw. Put the pressure pad stock in the tailstock chuck, with the smooth faced pad in place. Fit the toolrest in the lathe toolpost.

Centre the plain workpiece (the one without the hole) against the former and bring up the tailstock to exert pressure to hold it there. Quite a bit of pressure is required, as it is only the friction between the emery paper on the face of the former and the workpiece that will drive it. It is better to err on the side of insufficient pressure initially, and then increase it slightly if the work does show signs of slipping. With the simple, shallow shapes we are spinning, it is not a disaster if the work does slip. It can't fly off and any score marks are on the inside where they will never be seen. In fact the first signs of the brass needing re-annealing is the workpiece slipping slightly. It think it is better to err on the side of not overstraining the lathe. Metal spinning exerts quite a strain on the lathe, for which it was not really designed. If your lathe is one of the "mini" varieties, then it would be as well to restrict your spinning activities to lighter materials - say, metal of no more than 0.5 mm. thick. However, this will still produce a perfectly satisfactory pendulum bob.

Bring the toolrest to such a position that in levering the spinning tool against the fulcrum pin, you can move the working end of the tool from the centre to the lower (outer) edge of the workpiece in one clean, sweeping movement.

Try a dummy run without switching the lathe on. Only the flat face of the tool must touch the work, the round face would be used for spinning a concave surface or a hollow curve such as you might find on a bell.

Once you are satisfied that you can achieve the required movement in one sweep, smear some grease on the face of the workpiece plus a little on the flat face of the tool, and switch the lathe on at about 200 rpm. Press the tool against the work as near to the centre as the pressure pad will allow, and - without hesitating and with firm pressure - move it steadily down to the lower edge of the workpiece. Take about 3 seconds for this movement, and then repeat.

After this, the brass will feel a bit springy, so if the work is not yet lying snug against the former, remove it, clean off the grease, anneal it, and try again. At this second spin the work should come to a snug fit on the former, but do not be surprised if you have to anneal three or four times, particularly for your first attempt.

You will also find that the bob shell blank has stretched slightly and is now bigger than when you started. This is normal, and in fact will prove useful in this instance. The other point to note is always to work under the workpiece, so that is running away from the tool. Never apply a spinning tool at a point where the work is running towards you.

Swap the pressure pad for the one with the spigot, and spin the other shell by locating the spigot in the centre hole in the shell blank. Having spun this shell, use a sharp tool in the toolpost to machine its OD back to diameter. Take very light cuts, because the workpiece is only held by friction, and the type of brass being used might be a bit "sticky" to machine.

Clean off around the inside edge of both shells with emery to prepare for silver soldering. If desired, the edges can be thinned by rubbing the shells, face up, on a piece of coarse emery paper. Place the two shells together on your brazing hearth, and silver solder them together.

You can now see the reason for turning only one shell to diameter - it gives you a ledge on which to place the silver solder, thus ensuring a good joint.

Carefully file down the outer edge of the oversize shell by hand until it matches the turned diameter of the other shell. It would be nice to be able to do this in the lathe, but we have nothing to hold the work with, so it has to be done with files and emery.

The shell should now be "pickled", to clean it inside and remove all traces of flux, which will stain the brass if not removed.

Some Notes re "Pickling"

- If you have ever built a model steam boiler you will probably have pickled it in dilute sulphuric acid; the same stuff can be used here. If you do not have any of this hazardous substance in your workshop, and I don't blame you if you haven't, then for small jobs there are two readily available alternatives, and you won't have to sign the poisons register to get them!

- The first of these is citric acid. It is sold in dry powder form, and is readily available from chemists and home brewing suppliers. Mix it fairly strong, say about four teaspoons per pint of warm water. Soak the item to be treated in it for about an hour, and then rinse off well under running water. Citric acid is non-polluting and you can simply throw it away down the sink. Once mixed, it does not keep long, so make up a fresh batch each time, unless you know you are going to need it again within the next couple of days.

- The second alternative is caustic soda. This is quite a strong alkali, but is equally suitable for our purposes. It is readily available in super-markets, usually under a brand name (such as *Harpic*) for cleaning toilets and foul drains. It is also a dry powder and is mixed in the same proportions as citric acid. It can stain some brasses a pink colour, but this will polish out. When disposing of used caustic soda, be sure to pour it down the toilet to ensure that it goes into the foul sewage system where it will be broken down safely at the sewage treatment plant. Again, rinse the job well under running water. Citric acid is relatively harmless to the skin, but caustic soda can burn, so rinse your hands well after handling.

The pendulum rod, or the flat on a built up rod, will probably be about 3 x 6 mm. section, so two holes of this size have to be cut and filed at opposite points on the edge of the bob. Make sure they are located truly on the diameter of the bob, or the final result will look noticeably lopsided. Make the two holes a nice easy fit on the rod.

Now cut a piece of dry hardwood just slightly larger in section than the rod, so that it is a gentle push fit through these holes. Push it in one side and just out through the other.

You are now ready to fill the bob with molten lead. The wood dummy rod will char, but not burn, and will pull out fairly easily when the lead has cooled.

SAFETY WARNING:

- Casting lead is a hazardous business, and should be undertaken in a well ventilated area or out of doors, as the fumes from molten lead are highly poisonous. Make sure the bob or other item to be filled is firmly supported. Put the whole business on a large tray of some sort, so that if some lead does "escape" it cannot run off the bench and into your shoe.

- I promoted an old soup ladle for melting and pouring lead. I hammered a small lip for non-drip pouring, and riveted a small fence behind it to catch the dross on the surface of the molten lead. The ladle will safely hold a kilogram of molten lead, which is more than enough for the average pendulum bob. Melting is quick and easy, just hold the ladle over a large blowtorch, or a camping stove. Do **NOT** use an aluminium or light alloy ladle for melting lead - **it will melt at the temperatures involved!** Use an iron or steel receptacle.

▪ As noted above, you must "pickle" the bob after silver soldering, before you fill it with lead. You must also make sure the interior of the bob is dry before you pour in the lead. The smallest amount of moisture can flash into steam and spit molten lead at you - hideous facial burns are then a typical result. The best way to drive off any moisture in the bob assembly is to pre-heat it - not excessively, but definitely beyond the boiling point of water.

▪ Wash your hands and face after any lead casting session.

Fit the dummy wooden rod through the bob. Lay the bob flat, making sure that it is firmly supported, with the centre hole on top. Melt the lead and pour it in through the hole until it just overflows. Lead pours quite smoothly, and you should find that by holding the ladle with both hands you can easily pour through the small centre hole. Do it in one go - don't stop half way through to see how it's going. Any lead that overflows will not adhere to the outside of the bob, and the blob left protruding from the hole can be pared off with a sharp knife or chisel once it has cooled. Do not try to file it off, for you will probably mark the surface of the bob and spoil the finish left by the spinning tool.

Remove the wood rod and pickle the bob again, for about ten minutes, as you may otherwise get staining of the brass around the filling hole and the rod holes. Finally, clean the hole out with coarse needle files until the pendulum rod slides freely through it - you will probably find that it needs very little cleaning up.

One final thought on pendulums concerns the position of the rod through the bob. As described, and as illustrated in Fig. 43, the rod fits through the bob dead centre in side elevation. On some clocks, according to the maker's taste, the rod is set back slightly to the rear of the bob, so that the front face of the bob shows as a complete circle, with no cut-outs for the rod. If you want this effect, cut and file the

holes so that they are in fact slots in the edge of the back shell (the one with the hole in it), before silver soldering. Leave them a little undersize, and bring them up to finished size after soldering.

Motion Work

Motion Work is the name given to the under dial work which gives the 12:1 ratio required for the hands. The minute hand is mounted, via a friction clutch, on the centre wheel arbor, which turns once an hour. The hour hand is mounted on a sleeve collet, or *pipe*, which revolves freely on the centre arbor, and which is driven via what an engineer would call a layshaft. Fig. 45 shows the arrangement, which is identical to the backgear on your lathe. (The term "under dial work" covers any work - strike work, motion work, calendar work, etc. - fitted between the dial and the front plate.)

The cannon pinion, or cannon wheel, is riveted to the end of a long pipe called the cannon pipe. The assembly is free to revolve on the extended end of the centre arbor for hand setting, but is restrained from doing so by a friction clutch. This is simply a curved springy washer behind the cannon wheel, which locates on a shoulder on the centre arbor pivot. This shoulder is sometimes in the form of a square.

The outer end of the cannon pipe has a short square section which locates the minute hand, which will have a square hole in its centre. The minute hand is retained by a cup washer which is, in turn, retained by a taper pin through the end of the arbor. When the washer and pin are fitted, the cannon wheel

Fig 45 : <u>motion work</u>.

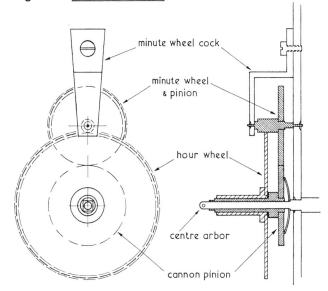

compresses the spring washer, such that it is firmly fixed to the centre arbor, but can be moved against the friction of the washer for hand setting.

The cannon wheel drives the minute wheel. This is sometimes called the reverse minute wheel and I prefer this name for it, as this eliminates all ambiguity. The reverse minute wheel is riveted on the reverse minute pinion, and the assembly is pivoted between the front plate and the reverse minute cock.

Sometimes the reverse minute wheel and pinion assembly is pivoted on a "post" screwed into the clock's front plate, with a taper pin through the end of the post to retain the assembly. This is a perfectly satisfactory arrangement, but it is difficult to do with small-count pinions of small modules, as the root diameter is restricted. It is, however, common on larger clocks such as longcases.

The reverse minute pinion drives the hour wheel. The hour wheel is mounted on a pipe which revolves on the cannon. On some clocks the hour wheel pipe revolves on another pipe; this pipe is fitted into a bridge piece which spans the cannon wheel, and which is known as the hour wheel bridge. This arrangement is usually reserved for higher class work, and is common on 8-day longcase clocks. The far more common system is that previously described, however, and it is a perfectly satisfactory arrangement.

It is convenient if all the motion work wheels and pinions can be cut to the same module. Obviously, for this to be possible, the centre distances of the two pairs of matching gears must be equal. This

Reproduction of a clock by Saloman Coster of 1657; the first practical pendulum clock.

condition can only be met if the sum of the tooth count of the cannon plus reverse minute wheel is equal to the sum of the count of the hour wheel plus the reverse minute pinion. The "usual" count is: Cannon 39: reverse minute 39, total 78: pinion 6, hour wheel 72, total 78. The gear ratios are thus 1:1 plus 12:1. Other ratios can be used, such as 3:1 plus 4:1, but the important point is that the centre distances of the two pairs of meshing gears must be equal, whatever the mixture of wheel counts and modules used.

Hands and Dials

As we have just discussed motion work, it is convenient to deal with hands next. Hands can be made from either brass or steel, according to taste, the need for visibility, and/or the desire for decorative effect. Brass hands are cut from "half hard" sheet of about 0.8 mm. minimum thickness. Fancy shapes are best cut with the piercing saw, but simpler shapes can be cut out with drills, hacksaw and files. They should be finished with very fine emery paper, followed by polishing, and burnishing of the edges. Steel hands are cut from carbon steel sheet down to about 0.5 mm. thick. A good source of steel well suited to the making of clock hands is the steel strapping or banding material used to strap pallets of bricks and other building materials. It is very tough, and although spring tempered, it can be sawn, drilled and filed at low speeds, and can be cut with a piercing saw well lubricated with candle wax or saliva.

Having cut and polished a pair of steel hands, they should be hardened and tempered if not already in that condition. You might question the need for hardening and tempering the hands, but if the friction washer has a fairly strong grip you will have to apply a fair bit of leverage when setting the hands by moving them from the tip, which is the natural way to do it. Hands are fine and can bend easily. Brass hands need hammer hardening, which is best done after cutting to shape, but before filing, finishing and polishing. Polish well before tempering, and do not get fingerprints on them. Temper to dark blue, and quench in oil. If you are using the previously mentioned steel strip, it will not need hardening, but must be polished and tempered to blue, and then quenched in oil. This second tempering of this material does not seem to affect the hardness of the steel. Quenching in oil keeps the colour better than quenching in water, and lessens the risk of subsequent rusting. Steel hands can be polished and left bright if desired, but in this case stainless steel is probably much the better choice of material, although some stainless steels are not easy to work. German silver can also be used, but it is a little soft for finely profiled hands.

When filing hands to shape, always use a filing button to shape the centre boss. If this is the least bit off centre or out of round, it will stick out like the proverbial sore thumb.

The minute hand is usually located on the end of the cannon by a square hole in the centre of its boss. Sometimes a brass collet is fitted to the centre of the hand with the square in the collet. This is useful in striking clocks because it allows fine adjustment of the position of the hand before riveting the collet in firmly. Hour hands almost always have a brass collet fitted. They can be simply bored to fit a slow taper on the hour wheel pipe, but a spring collet, as shown in Fig. 46, is a much more satisfactory arrangement. The hour hand should always locate just below the end of the hour wheel pipe to ensure that it does not rub against the back of the minute hand, which will often stop the clock. When the minute hand is firmly pinned in place, there should be a reasonable amount of endplay to the hour wheel pipe.

In mass produced clocks the dial is often fixed to the case, necessitating the removal of the hands before the movement can be taken out. In some cases the dial also has to be removed first. However, in the class of work we are likely to be doing, the dial is usually fixed to the movement by pillars which are pinned to the front plate. In some clocks, notably English Dial Clocks, the movement is actually suspended from the dial in this manner, and when one removes the dial from the case, the movement comes with it. In some longcase and some bracket clocks, it is the other way around: the movement sits firmly on a seatboard and the dial is suspended from the movement.

Dial pillars are turned up from brass bar, and are similar to movement pillars. A typical dial pillar is shown in Fig. 47. One end is riveted to the dial plate, while the other is pinned to the clock plate. Pinning is the normal method for holding dials, as access is often too limited for any other method. When riveting the pillars to the dial, take care that each pillar's cross hole is facing the edge of the movement plate, and that the pin will not be obstructed by any other part of the clock (e.g. movement pillars). The dial pillar should be well riveted down to the dial plate, and then filed flush and smooth. The holes for riveting the pillars are carefully spotted through from the

Fig 46 : hand collets.

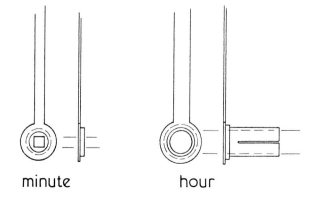

minute   hour

movement front plate before drilling, likewise the holes through the dial for the hands and the key.

Dials are typically "brass" or "painted". If you have a steady hand and a good eye for fine painting work, a painted dial can be quite attractive on the right clock. If you are not so talented, there are ways around the problem.

If you are going to paint the dial, then use steel or aluminium sheet for the dial plate, as brass does not hold paint well. Aluminium sheet needs a special primer, but apart from that, can be treated the same way as steel plate. For paint, use the aerosol cans sold for touching up car paintwork. Put on one undercoat, plus at least two topcoats. Spray evenly, and not too thickly. Leave 24 hours between coats. I find that a semi-matte finish gives best results.

As for colour, an off-white or slightly cream colour looks better than a brilliant white. The minute ring can be put on either with thinned paint in a pair of spring-bow compasses, or with waterproof Indian ink in the same, or in a draughtsman's pen. Tape a piece of thick card behind the centre hole to give yourself a centre for the point of the compasses.

Indian ink is surprisingly permanent, so do not make any mistakes! It can be scratched off, but even then it will leave a discoloured mark in the paint, and you will have to start again. The minute marks are best done by marking them out with the ai d of a protractor on a piece of thin card as a series of radial lines right across the card. The card is then cut to a circle slightly smaller than the minute ring on the dial, and stuck to the dial with a temporary adhesive or small pieces of masking tape. Be sure to get it dead centre. A straightedge can then be placed along the lines and two opposite minute marks can be drawn in at each position.

The numbers, or "chapters", can also be drawn in with Indian ink, using a stencil if required, but a much quicker way is to use dry transfer numbers, which are sold for use by draughtsmen and graphic artists. However, keep in mind that these transfers are susceptible to being scratched with a fingernail when setting the hands. Special transfers for clock dials were once available, but at the time of writing are unobtainable. Hopefully they will soon be

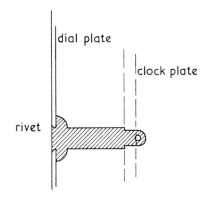

Fig 47 : dial pillars .

dial plate

clock plate

rivet

available again. Watch your horological supplier's catalogue.

It's a good idea to give the finished dial a coat of semi-matte clear varnish, to seal in the ink and dry transfers. The dial can then be kept clean in the future by wiping with a damp cloth.

An alternative to painting your own dial is to buy a commercially available printed, engraved or enamel dial, and to attach it to a blank dial plate. The pillars are riveted to the blank plate and the bought-in dial is fixed to the plate with either double sided sticky tape or a few tidy blobs of adhesive. The blank plate can be turned from 3 or 4 mm. thick sheet brass, with the centre recessed for the bought dial, so as to leave a brass rim about 3 mm. wide showing around the dial, both centring it and forming an attractive bezel.

If a keyhole has to be put in the dial, you may want to fit a standard commercial keyhole grommet. These are little brass or chromed rings which clip into the hole and give a nice finish to the dial.

I suspect that the average model engineer will be much happier with the traditional "brass" dial, as all the work of making this type can be done with his usual range of metalworking tools. The dial plate is typically a square or rectangle of brass sheet to which the dial pillars are riveted. An engraved and silvered chapter ring is attached to the plate, as are cast brass corner spandrels, if desired. Care must be taken to site the pillars where the riveted face will be hidden by the chapter ring when it is fitted. If this is not done, then the slight difference in colour between the two types of brass (in the rivet and the plate) will stick out like a sore thumb on a well polished dial. The corner spandrels are carefully positioned and clamped, then both spandrel and plate are drilled through 10 BA tapping size in two places, preferably where the hole is disguised by the pattern of the spandrel. One hole is tapped 10 BA and the corresponding hole in the plate opened out to clearing size. The other hole is fitted with a steady pin. The spandrel is then fixed in position with a single 10 BA brass screw from the back of the plate. Large spandrels are best fitted with 2 screws, while very small ones can dispense with the steady pin.

The chapter ring can be fixed in similar fashion with a 10 BA screw located on the 15 minute marks, where the minute mark is heavier than elsewhere.

Fig 48 : dial feet.

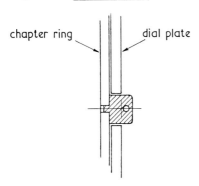

chapter ring   dial plate

The end of the screw is then easily disguised with a spot of black paint or Indian ink. An alternative to using screws is to fix "dial feet" to the back of the ring. They are turned up from 5 mm. brass rod and can also be located at the 15 minute points by means of a small pip in the centre of the foot, which locates in a corresponding hole in the ring. If the dial ring is of thick enough material, the locating hole can be blind. The foot can be fixed to the chapter ring with adhesive or soft solder paste. See Fig. 48.

In this instance the taper pins (whose presence in the scheme of things is indicated by the hole in the dial foot) do not pull the parts tightly together; leave just a little play to avoid straining the soldered or glued joint.

If you are soldering the dial feet, be careful not to overheat the chapter ring. Remove the iron as soon as the solder fuses, or you will damage the wax or paint filling in the engraving.

An 8 day Double Fusee Skeleton Clock - hour striking.

Dial Engraving, Waxing and Silvering

Chapter rings and spandrels of various styles and sizes are available from horological suppliers. If you have an engraving machine, or are adept at hand engraving, you can of course engrave your own brass dials and chapter rings. If you do not have these facilities or skills, and require a one-off design for a dial, then draw your design out on paper and get a commercial engraver to do the engraving for you. This can be expensive, but the quality will be first class, and you will have a unique dial, done to your own specification. I do not do my own engraving, so will not comment further on this process, beyond remarking that concentric circles and radial lines, e.g. a minute track, can be done on the lathe if the dial is not too big. Any engraving I require I have done by a professional engraver to my drawings and specifications.

I do, however, do my own waxing and silvering, both for my own clocks and in the course of restoration work. Wax sticks and silvering and finishing powders are readily available from horological suppliers.

The black wax is very similar to the old fashioned sealing wax. To apply it, the brass dial or chapter ring must be gently heated. If the dial is allowed to get too hot, the wax will burn. The easiest way to do the heating is over the gas ring on a cooking stove or a picnic stove. It is best if you can control the heat so as to warm the section you are working on just sufficiently to melt the wax. Rub the wax stick into the engraving. It is impossible not to get wax on the surface of the dial also, but this is not a problem. Scrape the excess wax off, or into more engraving, with a plywood scraper, but don't worry about removing every last trace at this stage. The solidified scrapings can be re-used.

Once all of the engraving has been filled with wax, the dial must be "grained" with wet-or-dry paper. This will also remove all traces of excess wax from the surface of the dial. Start with a paper with a grit of about 200. If you feel this grain looks a little coarse, give the dial another rub over with a finer paper, say 400 grit.

Remember that the grain must be visible. We do not want a highly polished surface or the silvering powder will not take so readily, nor will the finished job last as long.

Square or rectangular dials should be straight grained, top to bottom. With a circular dial or chapter ring, the grain should be concentric, and a simple little "graining jig" is required.

A baseboard is required, and a square piece of 12 mm. plywood just a little larger than the chapter ring is ideal. At the centre drive a nail to act as a pivot. Leave about 20 mm. sticking up and cut the head off. Procure another piece of wood, of about 25 mm. x 12 mm. section and a little longer than the radius of the chapter ring. Close to one end drill a clearance hole for the pivot nail. This is the polishing arm. Fix the chapter ring to the baseboard, face up, with a couple of pieces of double sided sticky tape. Centre it as well as you can by eye on the pivot nail.

Set the hole in the polishing arm over the nail and wrap a piece of wet-or-dry paper around the other end. The wet-or-dry paper can then be swept around the chapter ring, guided by the wood pivoting on the nail, to leave a nice clean and continuous circular grain.

The graining process will mark some of the wax filling and will also take the shine off it. The shine is readily restored by gently heating the whole dial until the wax melts once again, whereupon it will resume its nice shiny appearance.

The dial must next be thoroughly washed in warm, soapy water. Ordinary dishwashing liquid soap is quite suitable. After washing, rinse the dial thoroughly under clean running water, being careful not to touch the face with your fingers. From now on, the surface to be silvered must not be touched with the fingers, or the silvering powder will not take properly.

The silvering is done wet, so don't bother to wipe the dial dry.

The silvering kit, from your horological supplier, will consist of two packets of powder (both are white; don't mix them up). The silvering powder is silver chloride, usually mixed with a carrier, and the finishing/fixing powder will probably be cream of tartar - the same stuff you use in your kitchen.

> **Note:** Silver chloride is poisonous. Be very careful with it, and wash your hands well after using it.

Sprinkle some of the silvering powder on a small area of the wet dial and wrap a piece of close woven cloth, or chamois leather, around your index finger. Wet the cloth on your fingertip with clean water, and proceed to rub the powder well into the brass. Keep your fingertip wet and add more powder as required, gradually increasing the area covered until the whole dial takes on a dull, silvery-grey appearance. This process will take a few minutes, and when you think you have finished, it does no harm to go over the whole dial again, although you needn't take so long the second time. This second covering ensures that there are no thin spots on the silvering, which is only a micron or two thick. Rub the powder in with a small circular motion, gradually working your way around the dial.

Don't worry about the silvering process spoiling the wax filling. It will not "take" on the wax, nor will it spoil the surface. In fact, the wax may look shinier after silvering, but this is probably an illusion caused by the greater contrast between silver and black *vs.* brass and black.

Rinse the dial once more under running water to remove all traces of silver powder. Now sprinkle the finishing/fixing powder (or cream of tartar from your kitchen cupboard if you prefer) all over the wet dial and rub this into the surface in exactly the same way as you did the silvering powder. Unlike the silvering powder, this stuff is cheap, so don't be sparing with it. After two or three minutes of this treatment, rinse the dial once more under running water. The silvering should now have lost its grey appearance, and will have a nice, even, semi-matte finish all over. If any greyish patches remain, simply apply a little more cream of tartar or finishing powder.

If the dial is left in this condition, the silvering will last ten to twenty years, or more if well protected from the atmosphere, before showing signs of deterioration. However, although the process can be slowed down considerably, eventual deterioration is inevitable.

The traditional method of protecting the silvering from atmospheric degrading, and also physical damage, is by lacquering. Dial lacquer can be obtained from horological suppliers, and is normally based on shellac. It is effective, but is easily scratched with the fingernail when setting the hands. In time such scratches will show up as black

lines where the silvering has been exposed to the atmosphere.

A protective coating which has some advantages over lacquer is pure beeswax polish. This coating can be easily renewed every five years or so, and if scratched, it is, to a certain extent, self-healing - that is to say, the coating will slowly flow back into the scratch and continue to protect the silvering.

Whether you are going to use lacquer or beeswax, it is a good idea to first give the dial a rub over with yet another white powder - Bicarbonate of Soda (for which, raid the kitchen cupboard again!)

Bicarbonate of Soda is mildly alkaline, and will neutralize any acid left by the cream of tartar. It also tends to increase the whiteness of the silver, and give it a little more shine. It is rubbed into the wet dial in exactly the same way as the other two powders.

The beeswax is applied to the dial with a soft cloth which has been dipped into pure beeswax cream furniture polish. This polish can be purchased, or you can make your own beeswax cream by putting solid beeswax shavings into turpentine and letting them dissolve. Put in enough to make a fairly thick cream. When the resulting cream is used, the turpentine evaporates, leaving a coating of beeswax on the dial.

As noted earlier, this polish can be renewed by giving the dial a rub over every five years or so, without dismantling the clock. It is also easy to remove at any time, if you want to re-silver the dial. Simply give the dial a short soak in neat turpentine, and then a good wash in warm soapy water. Warm soapy water alone would probably be sufficient, without the need for turpentine.

Dial rings on ornate skeleton clocks are often fretted out into very elaborate patterns, sometimes to such an extent that it is difficult to tell the time shown by the clock! The numerals may be part of the piercing work, or they may be engraved, or applied, or small enamelled "shields" can be purchased for fixing at each hour position. With these ornate fretted dials, careful account has to be taken of where the dial pillars will be attached.

Dial Bezels

Bezels, if required, can be made by several methods. I speak here of bezels that would be used around the dial of a skeleton clock or regulator. The hinged and glazed bezels fitted to the wooden cases of many 20th Century clocks are a little more complicated, and can be readily purchased, so we will not concern ourselves with them here.

Bezels on quality clocks were usually of cast brass. If you have the facilities for pattern making, and for melting and casting brass, then there is no reason you cannot do this. A design such as "barley twist" can be produced on the face or edge of the bezel and will look very attractive. However, I suspect that most readers would prefer to know of a method other than casting.

A bezel is basically a large brass ring of "L" or "J" section, intended to fit around the outside edge of the dial and give it a "finished" appearance. A second, plain ring fits inside the bezel from the back to retain it. This retaining ring may be a firm push fit, or may be secured with pins or small countersunk brass screws. See Fig. 48A.

The bezel can be turned on the lathe from a disc of thick sheet brass. (It can be turned integrally with the dial plate, as already mentioned.) First secure a piece of plywood, say 20 mm. thick, to your faceplate. The brass sheet can then be secured to the plywood with 3 or 4 woodscrews. Turn the OD of the bezel, and then, using a trepanning tool (similar to a parting tool but with much more side and front clearance), plunge (carefully!) into the face of the sheet to form the inside profile of the bezel, in which the dial sits. You will probably need 2 or 3 cuts like this to form a wide enough slot before separating it from the sheet with a final plunge right through.

Next, reduce the OD of the plywood faceplate to a very tight fit inside the bezel. Push the bezel onto the disc and profile the front of the bezel to your taste: rounded edges, decorative rings, etc.

This method is somewhat wasteful of heavy gauge brass sheet. Spinning or forming from a much lighter sheet, say 1 mm., would be much more economical.

For both spinning and forming, the initial work required is the same. First mark out and cut a flat ring of 1 mm. brass with an ID equal to that required on the finished bezel and an OD to give enough metal to form the parallel portion. Bear in mind that the metal will stretch, so there is no need to cut it oversize. File the ID to a good finish and accurately to size.

Next, attach a piece of plywood to your faceplate, and from it make a "former" over which to shape the bezel ring from flat to cup-like form. First, turn the plywood to a diameter equal to that of your dial plate: a little more maybe, but no less. This is the ID of the parallel portion of the bezel. Next, turn a slight recessed seating on the edge of the face of the ply to locate accurately the ID of your embryo bezel. Make it a good fit on diameter but only half as deep as the thickness of the brass you are using. Finally - assuming you want a well rounded outside edge to the finished bezel - round over the edge of the plywood a little with a file while it is rotating in the lathe.

A second piece of plywood, to serve as a clamp over the bezel ring, is also required. Fix this second piece of plywood to the face of the first piece (which remains mounted on the lathe faceplate), using half a dozen woodscrews on a pitch circle just slightly under the diameter of the recess you made on the first piece of plywood. Now turn the OD of this second piece to 2 or 3 mm. less than that of the first piece.

The brass ring can then be sandwiched between the two pieces of plywood and held securely, but can easily be removed and replaced accurately if required.

Anneal the flat brass ring and put it in the sandwich. If you are going to spin it then that is the next operation. See the section dealing with pendulum bob shells for advice on spinning and the tools required. If you are going to form it by hammering, then remove the sandwich from the lathe and proceed to work the overhanging portion of the brass ring with a soft mallet, working your way all around the circumference with blows directed at a slight inward angle, and then repeating with blows directed at a slightly greater angle, for each successive pass around the job, until it lies close to the wooden former.

Whether you spin or beat, you will need to anneal the brass two or three times before the job is finished.

Fig 48A   BEZEL

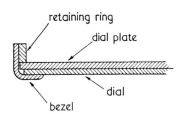

Once the brass is lying down evenly all around the edge of the plywood former, the sandwich is put back in the lathe (you would have removed it for forming), and the back edge, which will be a bit ragged, can be machined true and to correct depth with a parting tool or left hand knife tool. If you shaped the bezel by forming, it may be a good idea to take a skim off the OD to true it up. If you spun the bezel, the surface finish should be quite good enough as it stands and need no further work, except possibly the application of polishing papers and/or Autosol.

The bezel is retained on the dial/dial plate by fitting a retaining ring inside it from the back. This ring can be secured with 3 small countersunk brass screws put through the bezel radially into tapped holes in the ring, or with brass clock pins fitted in a similar manner and finished flush on the outside of the bezel. The neatest way, however, is to make the ring a tight push fit into the back of the bezel.

To make the retaining ring, cut a strip of 1.5 mm. brass just a little longer than would be required to fit around the inside of the bezel. Bend it around the former to the required diameter and carefully file one end down until it will just push fit into the back of the bezel when the two ends are butting squarely together, perhaps with a little help from a light clock hammer. It should need no further securing, nor will you need to solder the butted ends of the ring.

Casework and Finishing

I will not say much about making wooden cases. Those model engineers who are also adept at cabinetmaking will need no instruction from me. I'm no cabinetmaker, and my one simple rule when making a wooden case is, "How would I machine it if it was solid metal?" Having decided that, I usually do it that way.

Traditionally, clock case making was one step below "proper" cabinetmaking. The veneering and applied decorative work was first class, but the basic carcass was often quite simply held together with glue and nails, not fine joinery. The maxim seemed to be "If it doesn't show on the outside, don't worry what it looks like!" However, the workmanship, though basic, was not shoddy.

Do not make clock cases out of softwood. Use a close-grained hardwood such as oak or beech, and make sure it is well seasoned and dry. Old furniture is one source of supply. Get it cut and planed to your specification,and make sure the edges are square.

The stuff sold in DIY stores is generally not consistent enough for our purposes, although the moulding - scotia, OG etc. - can be useful and can be built up into more elaborate sections if required.

For joints I use a simple butt joint, reinforced with hidden dowels. Fig. 49 shows joints made this way, together with a simple jig to ensure that matching dowel holes are spaced accurately. Use the drill press and machine vise, plus clamps if necessary, to make sure all holes go in square. Use an accurate mitre box and a sharp tenon saw to cut the mitres and square ends.

If making a mitre joint with open dowels, hold both pieces of wood in a mitre clamp to drill for the dowels, and use the mitre clamp again when gluing. Use a water based glue, and wipe all surplus glue away from the joint with a damp cloth as soon as the joint is made. Make a couple of saw or file cuts along the length of the dowels before inserting them in their holes, to allow surplus glue and air to escape from the hole.

When you get to the sanding stage, always wrap your sandpaper around a block of wood. Failure to do so will result in rounded corners etc., and ultimate dissatisfaction with the job.

Finally, do not make the mistake of thinking that because wood is softer than metal you can cut corners, or that the job will be quicker or easier to do. Take the same care and time as you do when working with metal, and in the end you should be well pleased with the job.

Wooden cases can be painted, or stained and varnished, or stained and polished.

You may be surprised that I mention painting, but it was done quite a lot in the past, particularly on the country longcases, and of course it is the basis of japanning. If you want an "ebony" finish to the clock, painting is probably the easiest way, although it is certainly not true ebonizing as understood by an expert cabinetmaker or french polisher. For a painted finish, apply one undercoat and as many topcoats as you feel necessary, usually three, or maybe four. Brush the paint in well, and apply it quite thinly to avoid runs and dribbles. Sand down well between each coat.

Stain needs to be put on carefully to get an even colour. The first application will probably raise the grain slightly, so sand it down with fine sandpaper, and apply another coat if necessary. Varnish, like paint, should be put on thinly and well brushed in, sanding down between each coat until you have a result you like.

Stain and polish (actually, "stain and wax" would be a better term) takes a little longer. After staining, apply a good wax furniture polish - put it on thick, with a brush, and get an even coat all over, then lightly buff it with a soft cloth. Do not rub hard to start with. The cloth will drag on the polish, so rub lightly until it stops dragging, then you can rub hard and vigorously. Leave it a couple of days at least before applying a second coat of polish in the same way. It will need several applications before you get a really deep, good looking finish.

Painted or varnished cases also benefit from wax polishing. First, with very fine and worn sandpaper, lightly sand the case all over, and then apply the first coat of polish as previously described. Subsequent coats can be applied directly with a cloth, rubbed in well, and then buffed; this also applies to stained and polished cases once you have achieved the depth of finish you want.

Some of the foregoing might amuse a professional cabinetmaker, but I am a professional clockmaker who sometimes has to "do a bit of woodwork", and the methods described give me satisfactory results. I feel that most model engineers would consider themselves to be in much the same position, and I hope the advice offered here (as from one amateur woodworker to another!) will be found useful and encouraging. (I must also add that I apply the foregoing only to cases I have made for my own clocks. All wooden casework and restoration done on behalf of my clients is done by a professional cabinetmaker.)

Fig 49 : casemaking.

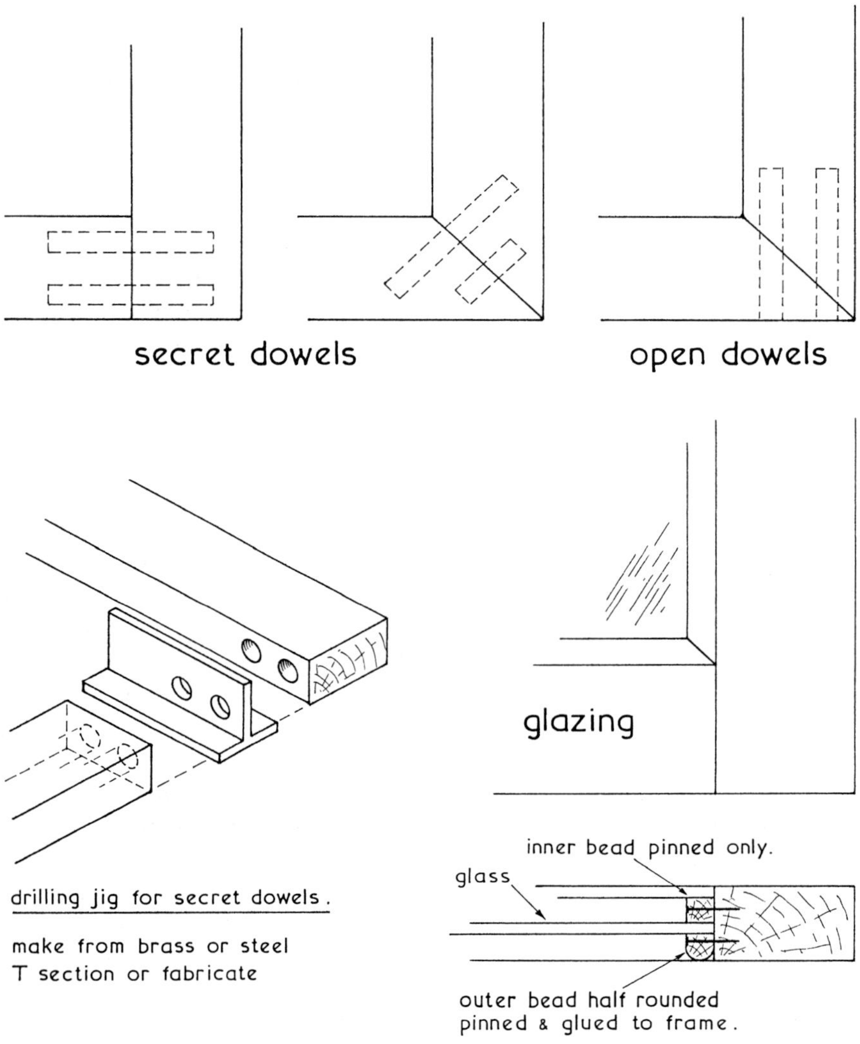

secret dowels   open dowels

drilling jig for secret dowels.

make from brass or steel
T section or fabricate

glazing

inner bead pinned only.
glass
outer bead half rounded
pinned & glued to frame.

Cleaning, Polishing and Final Assembly of the Movement

We should now consider the matter of cleaning, polishing and final assembly of our complete clock movement.

The polishing mediums I use are the aforementioned "Solvol Autosol" paste, sold in handy tubes for use by DIY motorists, and wadding impregnated with "Brasso", the well-known brass polish sold for household use. You will also need the following: white spirit, two soft cloths, two buffing sticks, a packet of wooden cocktail sticks, an old biscuit tin or similar full of sawdust, some paper kitchen towels, and a pair each of rubber and cotton gloves - both the usual household variety.

The buffing sticks are pieces of 3 mm. or 5 mm. plywood about 25 mm. x 150 mm. with a strip of felt glued on one side. As for the sawdust, boxwood dust is the traditional stuff, but almost any hardwood sawdust will do, if it is from seasoned wood. Softwood sawdust tends to retain the resin from the tree's sap, and is therefore not so good.

The brass plates, wheels, etc. will be covered with fingerprints and marks which are first removed with the "Autosol". Use one cloth to rub it on, and the other to rub it off. Next, take up some of your "Brasso" wadding, and rub all over the plates. Rub the worst of it off with the "dirty" cloth, and give a good polish with the clean one, holding the plate with the cloth.

From this point on, do not touch the plates, or any other polished item, with your fingers - wear the rubber or cotton gloves.

The wheels and other small pieces are easier to polish with the buffing sticks. Spread some "Autosol" on a stick with your finger and rub the wheel, or what have you, up and down the stick. You may find it easier - as I do - to rub the piece on the stick, rather than the other way around. Use the "clean" stick to polish the piece. Do not bother with Brasso-ing these small pieces.

A word of warning: do not use a motor driven "buffer" to polish the clock parts. Small parts are likely to end up suddenly embedded in the wall on the other side of the workshop. However, it is on the plates that a motorised mop will cause real damage, as it will very quickly pull the edges of pivot holes and oil sinks, and round off your nice square edges.

This spoils the look of the work, and will ruin your chances of winning a medal at the *Model Engineer Exhibition*! The only exception to this "no motorised polishing" rule is round parts such as pillars. Pillars and similar parts can be attached to a screwed mandrel held in the 3-jaw while polishing, but be very careful not to let a loose corner of the cloth catch in the lathe while it is running.

All the parts must next be washed in white spirit or turpentine substitute. Special horological solvents are available, but some of these are "active", and - if over-used - can do more harm than good to the shine you have so carefully worked for. White spirit and turps are cheap and readily available. There are also other readily available household solvents, but I have not tried them.

Do not be tempted to use petrol or lighter fuel. Apart from the danger of fire, they leave a discolouring film on the polished metal that is not easy to remove. White spirit does leave a slight deposit, but it is easily brushed off with a fairly stiff bristle brush. Turps does not leave a deposit but does not dry (evaporate) so readily. You pays your money, etc...

Wear your rubber gloves for this job, both to avoid fingerprints on the work, and to protect your hands; white spirit dries the skin and irritates any scratches or abrasions.

Fill an old frying pan with the spirit, and so far as is possible, immerse all the parts one by one, and brush well with a cheap paintbrush while in the bath. The aim is to remove every trace of polishing medium, so pay particular attention to all the holes.

When you are satisfied that a piece is clean, shake off surplus spirit and drop it into your tin of sawdust to dry it. When you take the piece out of the sawdust, shake or blow off any sawdust adhering to it, and then give it a really good brushing with a clockmaker's bristle brush. It is a good idea to rub the brush across a piece of chalk from time to time - this helps give a fine shine to the work.

Next, the pivot holes must be "pegged out" to make sure they are clean and dry. This is where the cocktail sticks come in. Clockmakers' pegwood can be purchased, but you can buy wooden cocktail sticks from your local supermarket. Push the tip of a stick into a pivot hole, give a few twists and pull it out. Do this from both sides of the hole. The wood should come out spotlessly clean. If it comes out dirty, shave off the dirty bits and try again. Repeat until the hole is clean.

At the maker's option, the plates, pillars, various cocks etc. can be lacquered or not. However, never lacquer wheels or other moving parts!

I do not lacquer my clocks. Having gone to great pains to ensure that all pivot holes are completely free of any foreign matter, I do not wish to risk bunging them up again with lacquer! If the brass is polished and not touched with the fingers, it will keep its shine for a surprisingly long time, particularly if it is protected inside a case or under a glass dome.

Having said that, for those who wish to lacquer, shellac lacquer is the type normally used. The plates are warmed slightly and the lacquer is put on thinly with a large flat soft brush or a cotton wool pad. As I do not do this, I can offer no further useful advice on the subject.

Before the clock is assembled, there is one more task to do, and that is to install the mainspring, weight, or fusee line, as the case may be. Let's deal with them in that order.

As purchased, mainsprings come to hand coiled up, with a piece of wire around the outside to contain them. They appear to be oiled, but this is in fact an anti-rust barrier. Some clockmakers advocate cleaning this off with turps substitute and sawdust before fitting, but in my experience this does not appear to be absolutely necessary. A mainspring will need oiling, but this is best done after fitting it into the barrel.

There is one very important point to note when handling mainsprings....

■ **Never** attempt to coil or uncoil an open spring, or to fit one into a spring barrel, or remove it from same, without using a proper mainspring winder. If you ignore this advice, the results can be very painful. A big fusee spring, suddenly released, can take your finger off; a smaller spring is quite capable of slitting your throat or wrist. Please do not treat this as an idle warning!!

Quite apart from what the spring may do to you, which may or may not involve permanent damage, you can also damage or distort the spring!

Mainspring winders can be purchased, but it is not difficult or time consuming to make one. Drawings of a simple but reliable one are available from my "Plans for Clockmakers" series of drawings. If you prefer to buy a ready-made mainspring winder, do not purchase one that does not have a proper hook

Fig 50 : <u>simple mainspring winder</u>.

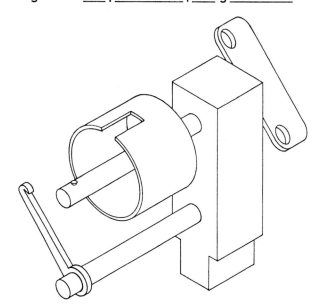

piece to hold the outer end of the spring. Do not rely on a clamping device or one that requires you to hold the outer end of the spring with a pair of pliers. Some rely on a ratchet to lock the spindle against the spring, while others use different methods. Whatever system is used, make sure it functions automatically, so that in the event of the key slipping in your fingers the spring cannot unwind itself more than half a turn at the most before the winder locks.

The winder is held in the bench vise. In using many types of mainspring winder, one first uses the tool to wind up the spring, then slips a slotted tube over the newly wound spring, and then carefully unwinds the spring into the tube.

The clock's spring barrel is then slipped over the tube and the outer eye in the spring is engaged with the barrel hook. The barrel is held firmly in a gloved hand, the spring is wound a couple of turns to release the tube, and is then unwound as far as it can go in the barrel, in a controlled manner. It takes no longer to do this than to write this paragraph.

The following are a few more injury-saving tips.

■ Always wear heavy duty leather or gardening gloves.

■ Wrap a cloth over the spring when first winding it up - this will help contain it if it does break.

■ Never stand in line with the spring. If it does break, pieces can fly off at speeds approaching that of a bullet. The workshop wall is more efficient at stopping such missiles than your face.

Fig. 50 shows a simple mainspring winder which locks by swivelling the key against a stop (not visible in this view) on the main post of the unit. In use it can only run half a turn before locking.

There are no such dangers in fitting weight lines, unless you drop the weight on your toe! The line is put through the hole in the barrel, and a simple "over and under" knot will prevent it from pulling out again. Assuming the weight is on a pulley, the other end of the line is either attached to a hook on the movement, or is fed through a hole in the seatboard, on which the movement sits within the clock case. Either way, a secure knot forming a small loop on the end of the line is all that is required. Feed the loop up through the hole in the seatboard, and poke a short piece of dowel through the loop. This will suffice to anchor the end of the weight line as long as the weight is on the line, and it is easily removed for servicing the clock.

A fusee line is a little more complicated. The line is secured in the fusee in the same manner as in a weight barrel. However, a conventional knot cannot be used in the spring barrel as there is not enough room. The barrel usually has three holes along the front edge for the line and it is secured as shown in Fig. 51. As the line pulls tight, it traps the short end and holds everything secure. Make sure these three holes are well chamfered, so that they will not cut the line.

A fusee clock is assembled with the line completely wound off both fusee and barrel. The spring barrel is then rotated to wind the line onto it as evenly and equally spaced as possible. This is one of those jobs that make you wish you had three hands. When all the line is on the barrel, the click is engaged and the spring is set up by putting (usually) one turn on the barrel arbor and then locking the barrel click with its pivot screw. The fusee is then wound slowly and carefully to ensure that it takes up the line without jumping a groove or two. As you near the end of the

winding operation, make sure that the stopwork is functioning properly. When fully wound, see that the last turn or so of line left on the barrel is lying evenly and straight around the barrel. As the clock runs down, the line will find its natural position on the barrel relative to the fusee groove, and henceforth it will automatically be in the right position to run straight into the groove.

While on the subject of fusees it might perhaps be wise to state that the only way to let down the spring of a fusee clock before disassembling or "taking down" is via the barrel ratchet and click. The click pivot screw is slackened slightly and the click disengaged and re-engaged manually while the spring is let down half a turn at a time with a key. (Another three handed job!) These big springs are very powerful, and if the clock has stopped in a fully wound position, the job needs to be done with great care.

Weight and fusee lines can be either stranded steel, stranded phosphor bronze, natural gut, or synthetic gut. All of these come in various diameters to suit the clock and the duty they have to perform. My own preference is for natural or synthetic gut, but it is just that - a personal preference - a gut feeling, as it were. The strength of natural gut cannot be guaranteed as can steel or synthetic gut, but it is nice to work with, and usually gives plenty of visible warning when it is nearing the end of its life.

Fig 51 : fusee line knot in spring barrel.

Clock Oiling

We now come to the subject of oils and oiling. The mainspring must be oiled before the clock is assembled, so I will deal with this task first.

There are considerable pressures and friction generated in a coiled spring, and a fairly heavy duty oil is called for. As it turns out, a standard motor car oil is quite suitable for this purpose. This stuff has additives to make it particularly suitable for its designed purpose, but these do not seem to be detrimental to the use we wish to make of it. If you prefer to use an oil without these "extras", a straight SAE 30 oil with no additives can be obtained from agricultural machinery dealers. However, I have used standard multi-grade motor oil for about 20 years now, and I have no reason to suspect it has had an adverse effect on any of my clocks.

The mainspring is fitted into the barrel dry. Before fitting the barrel cover, put 4 or 5 large dollops of oil on the coiled edges of the spring and put it aside for 10 minutes. Capillary action will draw it into the spring and it will be further distributed when the spring is wound. Make sure that there is enough, but do not over-oil, for the excess will only get squeezed out and drip everywhere, and this stuff seems to have the ability to run uphill!

Fit the arbor and barrel cover and put a drop of oil on the barrel pivots. Only a small drop is required here, and it is put on with an "oiler". This is simply a piece of piano wire of about 1 mm. diameter with one end hammered into a flat spoon shape. Make it about 100 mm. long, and fit it with a pencil sized handle. All the remaining oiling on the clock is done with this tool (although not with motor oil). You will find that with it you can pick up whatever size blob of oil you require - just dip the wire deeper into the oil to get more.

You can now assemble the clock for the last time - no more "dummy runs". As you do so, ensure that all the pivots run freely and have end play. Before the pallets are fitted, it should take very little pressure on the great wheel to make the escape wheel whizz around in either direction. As you assemble the clock, put a small drop of motor oil on the barrel arbor pivots and another small drop on the back of the ratchet to keep it from scoring the plate. Note that on a fusee clock, neither the barrel arbor pivots nor the barrel ratchet need oiling, as once the spring has been set up these parts will not move when the clock is going.

Having done the foregoing, you should wipe the oiler clean of all traces of motor oil, as all the remaining oiling is done with proper clock oil. Do not be tempted to use light machine oil, or sewing machine oil. It will lubricate the clock well enough for a while, but it has a tendency both to spread and evaporate. Clock oils are designed to stay where they are put, and will not evaporate for many years. I have seen clocks which were last serviced over twenty years ago, and the pivot holes still contain oil. It may be contaminated with atmospheric dust but it's still there.

Some pivots - e.g. the centre front pivot - will have to be oiled as you assemble the clock, as they will be inaccessible otherwise. Put on just enough oil to about half fill the oil sink - this will be ample. Oil all the pivots, and also put a blob on each of the pallet faces. These latter are easier to oil before fitting to the movement. Put a small amount on the crutch fork or pin where it impulses the pendulum.

It is debatable whether motion work needs oiling, as the forces involved are small. Put just the tiniest amount on the reverse minute pivots, and a small blob inside the hour wheel pipe. A tiny amount can also be put on the friction spring where it contacts the centre arbor shoulder and the back of the cannon wheel. The click pivot screw is oiled, also the back of the click against the plate, the end of the click spring where it bears on the click, and the end of the click in contact with the ratchet wheel.

That's it! Wind your clock up and it should tick away merrily.

This next piece of advice may sound strange to an engineer, but it is nevertheless sound advice: do NOT oil the wheel or pinion teeth. The brass wheels and steel pinions throughout the clock are intended to run dry, as the tooth form used creates very little friction. If you oil the teeth, the brass wheels will cut into the steel pinions. After a couple of hundred years this will slowly happen anyway, but oil actually hastens the process. The movement between contact points is relatively fast here, and oil, if present, would pick up dust from the atmosphere, form a fine grinding paste, and consequent wearing action would be similar to lapping, with which I am sure you are familiar.

Putting the Clock in Beat

The only thing which may be worrying you now is that the clock, instead of going at a steady tick-tock-tick-tock, is actually going tick tock - tick tock. If this is the case, the clock is said to be "out of beat".

This is corrected by bending the crutch. Some high class clocks have a built in beat setting adjustment, but the vast majority do not, and bending the crutch is the accepted way of correcting this fault.

A clock which is out of beat, apart from not sounding right, will probably not run its full eight days, or for whatever period it was designed, and time-keeping will suffer. Watch the clock carefully and note which pallet is allowing the longest pause between ticks. That pallet is moving too deep into the escape wheel, and this is corrected by bending the crutch *away from that side.*

You will probably find it does not take much movement to correct this. Be careful not to exert pressure that will damage the pallet arbor pivots. The tool shown in Fig. 52 will enable you to hold the top end of the crutch steady while you push the bottom end with your finger. Make the tool from mild steel. The two different size slots are to suit different sizes of crutch.

If the clock has been made with care, the only other thing likely to stop it is friction where there should be none. For example, are the hands clear of the dial?

Fig 52 : crutch bending tool.

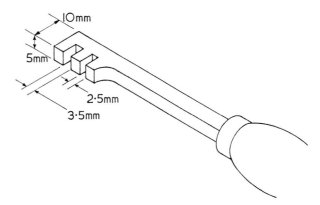

Are the hands clear of each other? Does the hour pipe have end play? (It should.) Is the crutch pin stiff in its slot, or the fork tight on the pendulum rod? Do they have too much play and waste energy?

It is unlikely that a newly made clock will have any of these faults, but these are the sorts of tiny things which can stop it.

So there it is! If you have read this far, I would hope that you are now inspired with the knowledge and enthusiasm to make the necessary clockmaking tools, and then to build your first clock. Once you have the tools, you'll probably want to use them again. It can be addictive, but is not harmful to health!

Happy Clockmaking!

Appendix I
A Little Bit of Theory

Virtually all of the foregoing has been concerned with "how" rather than "why". I believe a little bit of basic knowledge of clock gear trains and the properties of pendulums will not come amiss, and may in fact be quite useful if you are restoring an old clock which may have parts missing, rather than building a new one from a set of working drawings.

Let's deal with the pendulum first, as its length - and therefore its beat - is usually decided first when designing a new clock, and the resultant decision then bears directly upon the design of the wheel train.

The "theoretical pendulum" consists of a bob of infinite mass suspended on a rod of zero mass. This is obviously impossible to achieve, so for practical purposes a quite simple calculation to find the length and beat of a pendulum will suffice.

A one second pendulum is about 994 mm. long from the point of suspension to the centre of the bob, although in fact it actually varies slightly, depending on where you are in the world. In practice it always has to be a little longer than the theoretical length, because the mass of the rod has the effect of raising the centre of gravity of the complete unit above the centre of the bob.

Because the pendulum is suspended by a spring, the first few millimetres of which do not move when the pendulum swings, the actual "point of suspension" is also ill defined.

For these reasons it is best to make a new pendulum about 3% longer than one's calculations suggest. If found necessary, it is easy to shorten the suspension spring, the rod or the rating thread to bring the clock to time. It is not so convenient to lengthen a newly made pendulum!

The beat of a pendulum is proportional to the square root of its length, or - put the other way round - its length is proportional to the square of its beat. In other words, a half second pendulum is one quarter the length of one beating full seconds; a pendulum beating one third of a second is one ninth, etc..

If you know the beat you require from a pendulum, the simplified formula for determining its length is:

$$L = CS^2$$

where   L = length in millimetres, or inches, depending upon which system one pleases to use;

C = Constant: 944 mm. (or 39.134", for Imperial units)

S = Duration of beat in seconds.

If you wish to have a pendulum beating 0.4 of a second, the equation is:

$$L = 994 \times 0.4^2 = 159.04 \text{ mm.}$$

or... $L = 39.134 \times 0.4^2 = 6.261"$
in Imperial units

If you have a pendulum of given length and wish to know the duration of its beat, then

$$S = \sqrt{L/C}$$

Say you have a pendulum of length 300 mm, then

$$\sqrt{300/994} = 0.549 \text{ seconds.}$$

When measuring the length of an existing pendulum, you should measure from the centre of the bob to a point about one third of the way down the suspension spring from its effective suspension point, which is usually the bottom edge of the top cheeks. There is usually ample length of rating thread for corrective adjustment of small errors of estimation.

I am sure most model engineers know that the overall ratio of a gear train is found by dividing the product of the tooth count of the driving gears by the product of the tooth count of the driven gears.

As a simple example, let's consider the primary wheels in a clock train - that is, the drive from the spring barrel to the centre arbor.

The centre arbor has to revolve once an hour, and most springs will generate about 12 complete turns within the barrel. We wish to use about 6 of those turns to drive the clock for 8 days. In 8 days there are

192 hours; 192 divided by 6 (turns of the spring) = 32. This number tells us we need a ratio of about 1:32 between the great wheel and the centre arbor. If the great wheel has 72 teeth, the intermediate or "8 day" pinion 12 leaves , coupled with a wheel of 64 teeth, and the centre arbor pinion has 12 leaves, the equation is:

$$\frac{72 \times 64}{12 \times 12} = 32$$

This gives us exactly what we want - a ratio of 1:32.

The timekeeping part of the train, from centre wheel to escape wheel, is a little more complicated, because we also have to take account of the beat of the pendulum, which is dependent on its length.

Let us start from scratch and assume we want a clock with a (theoretical) pendulum length of about 150 mm. Using the pendulum formula already given, we find that a pendulum of this length has a beat of 0.3884 seconds.

This has to relate to the centre wheel, which must turn once an hour, so we divide the number of seconds in an hour - 3600 - by 0.3884. The answer is 9268, ignoring the figures after the decimal. This is the number of times the pendulum must beat in one hour. Put another way, it is the number of times we want the pendulum to beat for one revolution of the centre wheel. So we now know that the overall ratio we are looking for is 1:9268.

We must also remember that the pendulum only passes "half a tooth" of the escape wheel for each beat, hence the number of teeth on the escape wheel must be multiplied by 2 in the equation. If this sounds confusing, remember the longcase clock with a pendulum beating seconds - its escape wheel has only 30 teeth, yet revolves once a minute - 60 seconds.

Let us try the following wheel count:

Centre wheel: 80 teeth
"Third" wheel: 72 teeth; pinion: 7 leaves
Escape wheel: 40 teeth; pinion: 7 leaves

The equation becomes:

$$\frac{80 \times 72 \times (40 \times 2)}{7 \times 7} = 9404$$

The pendulum would therefore beat 9404 times per hour. The number we require is 9268, but we will continue with the figure just arrived at. 3600 (seconds per hour) divided by 9404 (beats per hour) is 0.3828, which is the duration of one beat, in seconds.

From the pendulum formula, $L = CS^2$, we can calculate the theoretical length of pendulum required for the wheel train in question. We do so:

$$994 \times 0.3828^2 = 145.65 \text{ mm.}$$

This is in fact near enough to the length we were looking for, 150 mm., to make very little practical or visual difference.

To lengthen the pendulum slightly, we should reduce the number of teeth in one (or some) of the wheels, or increase the count of one of the pinions. This latter alternative will have a much more dramatic effect on the answer. The logical change to make is to reduce the centre wheel tooth count to 78. If we do so, what happens?

$$\frac{78 \times 72 \times (40 \times 2)}{7 \times 7} = 9168.9$$

giving a beat duration of 0.3926 seconds, and a pendulum length of 153.23 mm. This would probably be equally suitable, but remember that the actual pendulum usually works out slightly longer than the theoretical one.

By counting the wheel and pinion teeth, and re-running the above calculation, you can also work out the length and beat of a missing pendulum for an existing clock.

This equation can also obviously be used to determine the count of a missing wheel, assuming you have, or know, the length or beat of the pendulum. Even if you are not sure of the pendulum's beat, you can work your way around to it by intelligent guesswork to start with, and a few minutes with a pocket calculator.

To find the count of a missing wheel, the same equation as before is used, obviously leaving out the unknown number. The answer is then divided into the number of beats per hour.

Taking the wheel count and resultant pendulum beat used in the last example, let us assume that the "third" wheel is missing. We run the equation again, but without the missing third wheel count (we obviously don't enter any figure into our calculator for the question mark).

$$\frac{78 \times ? \times (40 \times 2)}{7 \times 7} = 127.3469$$

The answer is in effect the hourly beat of a pendulum using that shortened train. The ratio of that beat to the beat we know we require will be the tooth count of the missing wheel. Therefore, if we divide our answer into 9168.9, then

$$\frac{9168.9}{127.3469} = 71.999$$

As we cannot have 0.999 of a tooth - we either have a tooth or we don't - the correct answer is obviously 72, the tiny error arising from rounding off the decimal places. Even if we round off to the nearest whole number we still have an answer close enough to leave no doubt, thus:

$$\frac{9169}{127} = 72.1969 \text{ which can be rounded off to 72}$$

Our answer is easily cross-checked by running through the first equation again, inserting our number of 72 in place of the question mark. This will show our calculation is correct, by giving us the beat we need, namely 9168.9.

Incidentally, the wheel following the centre wheel is always called the third wheel. This is because in the old weight driven movements it always was the third wheel in the train. The name has survived, regardless of the number of wheels in the train.

Back to our sums - let us do the same calculations but assume that a pinion is missing:

$$\frac{78 \times 72 \times (40 \times 2)}{? \times 7} = 64182.857$$

This answer might seem more confusing than the one we had for the missing wheel, but it is in fact the same thing. The ratio between the answer and the beat we know we need is the tooth count of the missing pinion. This time, because the pinion is the driven gear, we divide our answer by the beat we know we require. (We did the opposite in the first example, where the missing wheel was a driver.)

Therefore,

$$\frac{64182.857}{9168.9} = 7.00006 \text{ which we can round off to 7.}$$

If, in your haste, you do this division "the wrong way round", you will get a "funny" answer, in this case 0.1428, which is the reciprocal of the answer you require. Simply press the 1/x button on your calculator to obtain the correct answer - 7 - which would be the number of leaves in the missing pinion.

What if the complete wheel and pinion are missing?

Then

$$\frac{78 \times ? \times (40 \times 2)}{? \times 7} = 891.4286$$

and

$$\frac{9168.9}{891.4286} = 10.28$$

The answer in this case is the ratio between the missing wheel and pinion. It is reasonable to assume that at this point in a clock train the missing pinion will have the same count as the next one along, which is 7. Therefore

$$7 \times 10.28 = 71.999, \text{ which we would round off to 72.}$$

We would thus know the tooth counts throughout the complete train.

As can be imagined, there are many more formulae involved in clock work. Some concern the strength of materials, the properties of mainsprings and balance springs, compensated and isochronous pendulums, and so on.

The latter topic still occupies great minds after 300 years, as does the design of the ideal fusee curve before you cut metal.

In spite of the quartz crystal clock, there is still much research and experimental work that can be done with mechanical clocks. Like the steam engine, they may be "dead", but they obstinately refuse to lie down. They possess a fascination that the quartz clock will never have.

Appendix II
A Selected Bibliography

Title/Author	Publisher
Watch and Clock Making and Repairing W.J. Gazeley, FBHI	Robert Hale
Clock and Watch Escapements W.J. Gazeley, FBHI	Robert Hale
The Science of Clocks and Watches A.L. Rawlings	British Horological Institute
Gears for Small Mechanisms W.O. Davis	TEE Publishing
Clock Design and Construction Laurie Penman	Argus Press
Practical Clock Repairing Donald de Carle, FBHI	NAG Press
Watch and Clock Encyclopedia Donald de Carle, FBHI	NAG Press
The Clockmaker, Vols. I and II	TEE Publishing
Clock Wheel and Pinion Cutting J. Malcolm Wild, FBHI	TEE Publishing
Making an Eight Day Longcase Clock A. Timmins, FBHI	TEE Publishing
The Amateur's Lathe L.H. Sparey	Special Interest Model Books
The Model Engineer's Workshop Manual George Thomas	TEE Publishing
A series of books describing the construction of a number of individual clocks: John Wilding, FBHI	Rite Time Publishing

The publisher of this book stocks all of the above titles which are in print, along with other horological and engineering titles.

TEE Publishing usually have secondhand copies of those titles out of print.

Appendix III
Specialist Material Suppliers

All model engineering suppliers carry a good stock of brass rod, silver steel, gauge plate, mild steel rod and sheet and "half hard" brass sheet. Some carry a limited range of clockmakers' engraving brass. A specialist with a large range of clockmakers' brass and other materials including BA screws is:

Ian T. Cobb. Horological Engineer
8 Poplar Avenue,
Birstall,
Leics. LE4 DU

Horological wheel and pinion cutters, form relieved multi-tooth in HSS, are available from the manufacturer:

P. Thornton Ltd.
The Old Bakehouse,
Upper Tysoe,
Warwickshire, CV35 0TR

Ian T. Cobb (above) will supply ready cut wheels and pinions for those unable to do this work themselves.

General clockmakers' and repairers' supplies: almost everything you will need, including mainsprings, dials, weights, lines, pendulums etc.; also a good range of tools and books:

Meadows and Passmore Ltd.
1 Ellen Street,
Portslade,
Brighton,
E. Sussex, BN41 1EU

(The above company has no minimum order requirement and uses a fixed scale of post and packing charges - a very good policy.)

Specialist tools, including dividing plates:

J.M.W. Clocks
12, Norton Green Close,
Sheffield,
S8 8BP

Engraved and silvered chapter rings and complete dials for longcase and bracket clocks, cast brass spandrels etc. are obtainable from Meadows and Passmore (above).

There are many more suppliers to the horological trade who are also happy to supply amateurs.
All advertise from time to time in the horological magazines - "Clocks" and "Horological Journal".

Appendix IV
The Clock

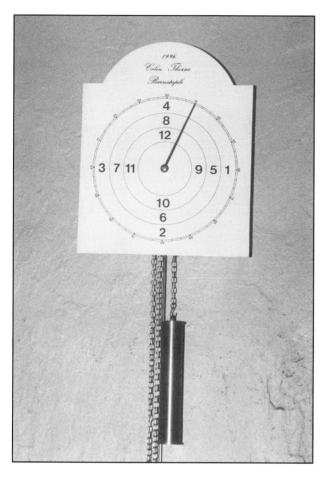

The Benjamin Franklin clock
(Front)

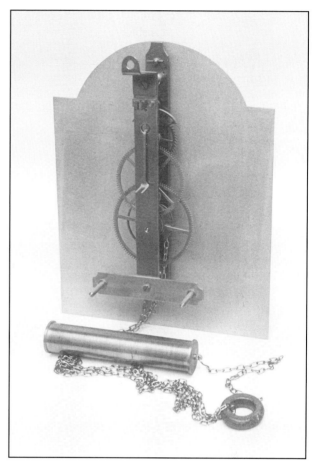

The Benjamin Franklin clock
(Back)

It would seem appropriate that a book on making clocks should contain drawings of "a simple clock" as an encouragement to readers actually to start cutting brass instead of just thinking about it. The following pages give full details of a clock designed by Benjamin Franklin. (Yes, the same Benjamin Franklin who went kite flying in a thunderstorm!)

Clocks don't come much simpler than this one. It has only 3 wheels and 2 pinions, no motion work, and therefore only one hand, which indicates both hours and minutes. This one hand makes one revolution every 4 hours, and it will be seen, for example, that the 12 o'clock position also indicates 4 o'clock and 8 o'clock. This has the possibility of causing confusion, and is probably why the idea never caught on, but it does made an interesting clock, and one that will certainly be a talking point, if nothing else! With

weight drive and recoil escapement, it will also be a good timekeeper, probably within +/- 1 minute per week or better.

The drawings detail a "cottage" version of Franklin's clock. There is no casework or dust cover, but the movement is robust enough to stand up to quite a lot of atmospheric pollution. I have altered Franklin's wheel count slightly to enable a reasonably large module to be used for the teeth, but at the same time keeping the great wheel to a size that can be machined in a small lathe such as the Unimat.

Although the quantity of work (and materials required) is much less than for a conventional clock, the variety is much the same. If you can build this one, then you can build any clock. If you mount it on the wall to give 2 metres clear drop to the weight, it will run for about 4 days on one winding. Hook the free end of the chain to the bottom of the front plate to stop it "escaping" if the clock does run right down. A ring counterweight is also used on the free side of the chain to keep a small amount of tension on it to avoid "knotting".

All the work involved in making this clock has been described in previous chapters. The only part which may put some model engineers off is the painting and numbering of the dial, but if the methods detailed in the chapter on hands and dials are followed, success should be assured.

The dial plate is detailed to be cut from 1 mm. mild steel sheet, but could just as well be aluminium or brass. Brass is more expensive, and does not take paint well, but aluminium would be OK if 1.5 mm. sheet was used. Whatever you use, de-grease it with white spirit, and rub with medium grade emery to provide a key for the paint.

A few other comments might not come amiss. The clock weight is hung from a chain, rather than a line or cord, and we have not previously mentioned this particular type of drive.

The teeth or pins of the chain wheel engage every second link of the chain, while every other link rests in the groove. When making the pins it is a good idea to make them slightly over length, and test with the chain before finishing. They must be long enough to engage the chain positively, but if they are too long they will tend to lift the chain off. This is another of those items which must be made to fit rather than made to plan, as individual chains may differ slightly in pitch etc. The chain quoted is a standard clock chain of 6 mm. pitch (50½ links per foot), the pitch being the internal length of the link. Do not be tempted to cement or solder the pins into the wheel; sooner or later you - or more likely some future repairer - will need to renew them because they have become worn. Believe me, if you have "glued" them in, he won't thank you for it!

The pinions are shown on the drawings as being turned integral with the arbor. With pinions this small, it is a little risky making them as separate pinion heads to be Loctited to the arbor, because of the small amount of metal between the root diameter of the pinion and a practical arbor diameter. If you do decide to make separate pinion heads, then use no larger than 2 mm. diameter rod for the arbor. Even then there will only be 0.35 mm. thickness of metal left at the root of the tooth space. I recommend integral pinions as on the drawing.

However, with integral pinions you won't be able to depth them in the small escapement depthing tool shown in Fig. 38, but will need a "proper" depthing tool. However, if you do not have one of these, do not despair! With only two meshing wheels/pinions, this point of possible loss of power does not loom quite so large in importance as in an 8-day timepiece with a more complex wheel train. Cut the wheels and pinions dead to specification on outside diameter, and mark the centres on the plates as accurately as possible to their theoretical centre distance. These measurements are given on the drawings. If you have a vernier height gauge, you should have no trouble marking out - but do use the most accurate method you have. One way is to set the small depthing tool to distance using a vernier or dial calliper gauge, by measuring over the runners and adding the diameter of one runner (assuming they are both the same diameter).

I have found that using and marking out with the depthing tool, I will usually be well within 0.1 mm. of true theoretical centre distance. With careful marking out, plus similar care taken in centre punching and drilling accurately, you should have no problems.

I have detailed the pallets to be fixed to the arbor with an 8 BA cheesehead screw. This, or something similar, is often done on quality work, and has the advantage that when the pallets do eventually wear, they can easily be moved along the arbor a little way, so as to present a new face to the escape wheel. As previously mentioned, the pallets can also be secured with "Loctite", soft solder, or a drive fit - use whichever method you prefer.

The single hand is mounted on a split collet similar to a conventional hour hand. This is sufficient to retain the hand, but a conventional domed washer and clock pin are also used to ensure that the hand cannot work its way off when setting to time. In this clock the pin is simply a retainer, not a "fixer", and there should be the smallest amount of play to the domed washer. The pin should not cause any additional friction between collet and arbor.

The pendulum bob detailed is a spun brass shell with lead centre as detailed earlier in this book. This is perhaps a little fancier than might be usual for a cottage clock, and it is also too large to be spun on a small lathe. However, if you prefer, you could use a standard cast iron, or lead, replacement bob for a longcase clock, as that type will fit this pendulum, and will perhaps be more in keeping with the overall style. These bobs can be obtained with an "as cast" finish or with a brass face.

It would be as well to make the pendulum rod about 10 mm. over length initially, and see how the clock keeps time. The difference in mass between lead and cast iron can affect the ultimate position of the bob on the rod, as can the actual size of the bob. The lighter the bob, the further down the rod it must go to compensate for the mass of the rod. As noted earlier, it is easy to shorten a rod - not so easy to lengthen it.

The pendulum bottom flat can be made by either of two methods. The threaded part at the end of the piece can be turned as an integral part of the rectangular brass bar material, giving you a one-piece flat. Alternatively, the end of the flat can be drilled and tapped to receive a piece of 4 BA studding secured with "Loctite". Either method is acceptable.

The suspension spring is a non-standard size and will have to be made, although a long-case suspension spring could be modified by shortening and fitting a new (second) cheek. A good source of spring steel of this thickness is double edged razor blades, as used for shaving. If you use one, you will find it is easily shaped by snapping and then grinding. However, you will have to anneal the ends for drilling. Push the razor into a potato, leaving exposed only the portion to be annealed, so as not to draw the temper below the ends of the cheeks.

The weight is lead in a brass case, which is perhaps more in keeping with a Vienna Regulator than a cottage clock, but it will match a brass faced pendulum bob, if that is what you have decided on. A standard cuckoo clock "fir cone" weight would also suit this type of clock, or even an uncased lead weight. The clock will need about 750 g. to drive it, but do run a "loaded baked bean tin" test before you make or buy a weight.

A brass-cased weight of the dimensions given will weigh about 80 gm. for every 10 mm. of length, so this will give you some idea of how long you should make it, should you decide to do so.

Do not use a weight of more than 40 mm. diameter, or it will interfere with the free end of the chain, and possibly with the pendulum bob also.

30 hour Benjamin Franklin clock in wood wall case; the bottom panel contains a mirror.

The drawings carry metric dimensions, but for stock materials the nearest Imperial equivalent will do if necessary, e.g. ⅛" for 3 mm. Use the materials you have, or can get easily, and make appropriate adjustments, e.g. for parts that have to be riveted in place. I find the metric system very convenient to work with in both designing and making clocks.

Materials List

NOTE: In this list, no allowance is made for chucking pieces on the rod and bar lengths, so you will need more than the exact amounts shown.

Brass Sheet

6 x 20 x 20	Backcock
3 x 210 x 45	Plates
3 x 35 x 70	Weight shell caps
2 x 110 x 110	Spike plate, Great wheel, Click spring
1.5 x 65 x 85	3rd wheel
1 x 100 x 55	Escape wheel, Crutch
1 x 125 x 250	Pendulum bob
0.4 x 40 x 5	Suspension spring cheeks

Brass rod and bar

ø35 x 10	Chain wheel
ø25 x 7	Counterweight
ø10 x 70	Pillars
ø8 x 70	Dial feet, Collets
ø1.6 x 50	Chain wheel pins
5 sq. x 15	Pendulum top block
10 x 5 x 165	Pendulum flat
ø12 x 12 *or* 12 A/F x 3	Rating nut to suit bob
ø20 x 10	Great wheel collet

Thin Wall Brass Tube

ø30 x 120	Weight shell

Mild Steel Sheet

2 x 15 x 6	Click
1.5 x 20 x 60	Hanging bracket
1 x 200 x 250	Dial plate

Mild Steel Rod

ø6 x 6	Click screw
ø3.5 x 550	Pendulum screw

Silver Steel Rod

ø8 x 70	Spikes
ø6 x 70	Arbors and Pinions
ø5 x 50	Centre arbor
ø2 x 35	Pallet arbor

Gauge Plate

3 mm x 50 x 25	Pallets

Steel Screws, Cheesehead

4 off 4 BA x 6 mm.
2 off 6 BA x 6 mm.
1 off 6 BA x 5 mm.
1 off 8 BA x 4 mm.
1 off 10 BA x 2 mm.

plus **assorted Clock Pins**

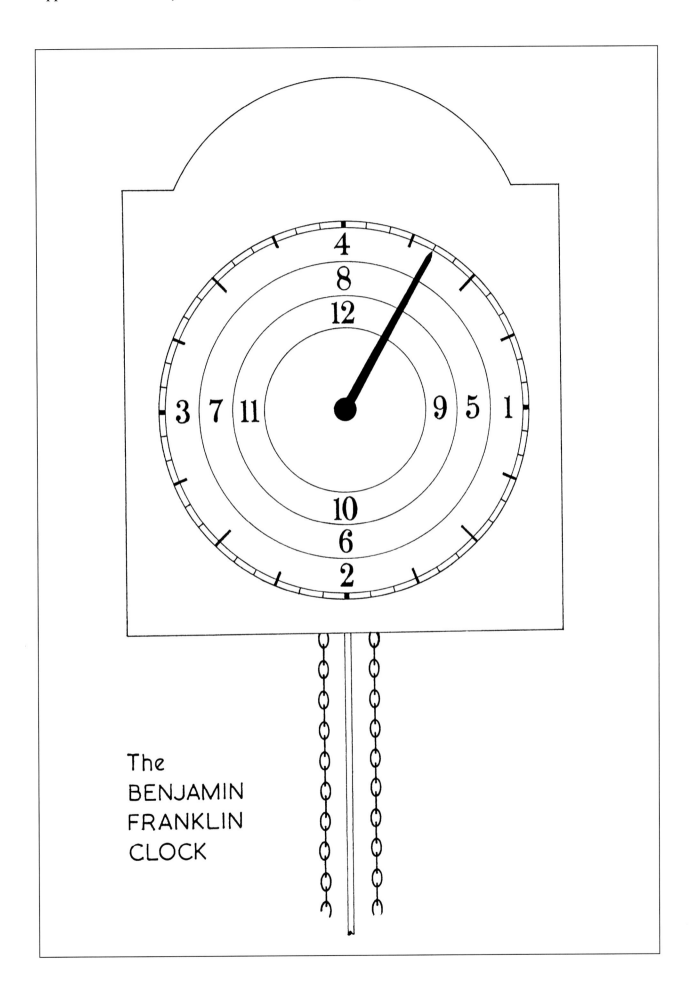

The
BENJAMIN
FRANKLIN
CLOCK

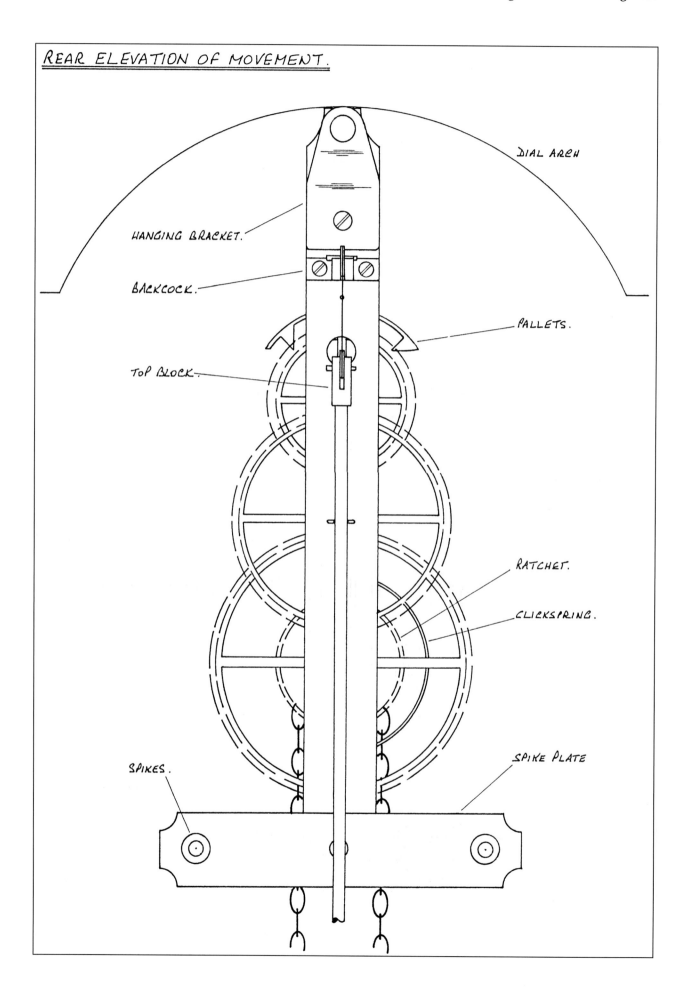

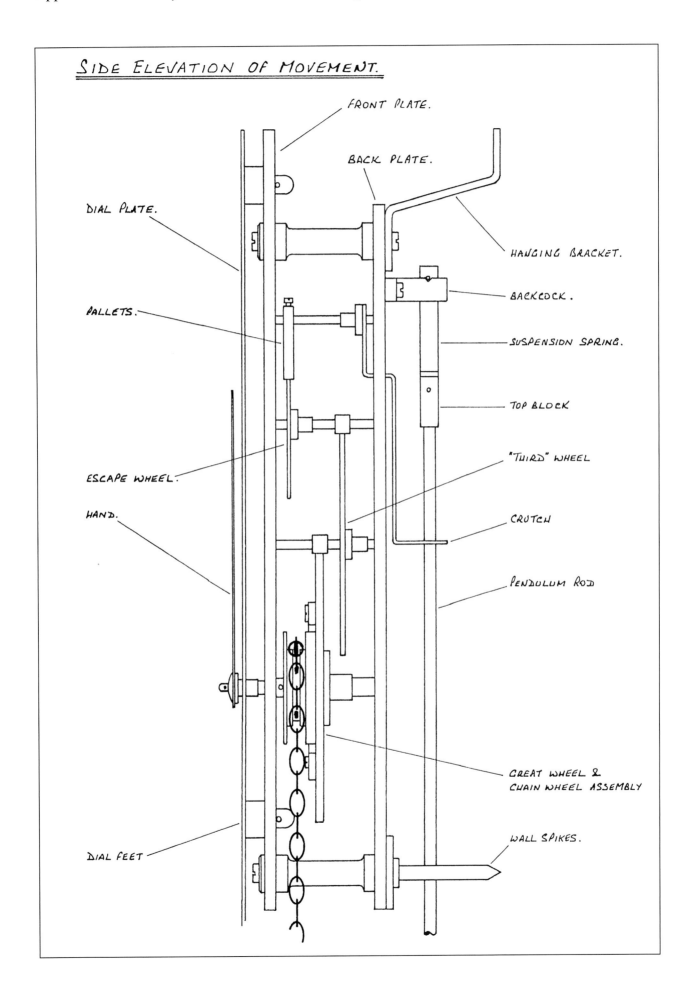

SIDE ELEVATION OF MOVEMENT.

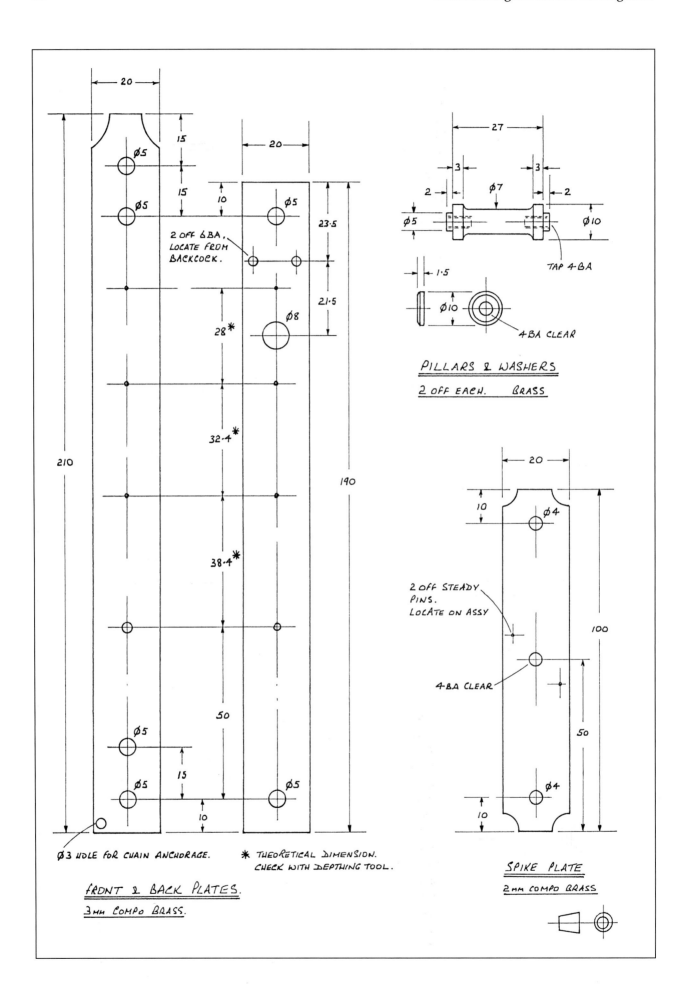

2 OFF 6BA,
LOCATE FROM
BACKCOCK.

TAP 4-BA

4-BA CLEAR

PILLARS & WASHERS

2 OFF EACH.   BRASS

2 OFF STEADY
PINS.
LOCATE ON ASSY

4-BA CLEAR

Ø3 HOLE FOR CHAIN ANCHORAGE.   * THEORETICAL DIMENSION.
                                        CHECK WITH DEPTHING TOOL.

FRONT & BACK PLATES.

3MM COMPO BRASS.

SPIKE PLATE

2MM COMPO BRASS

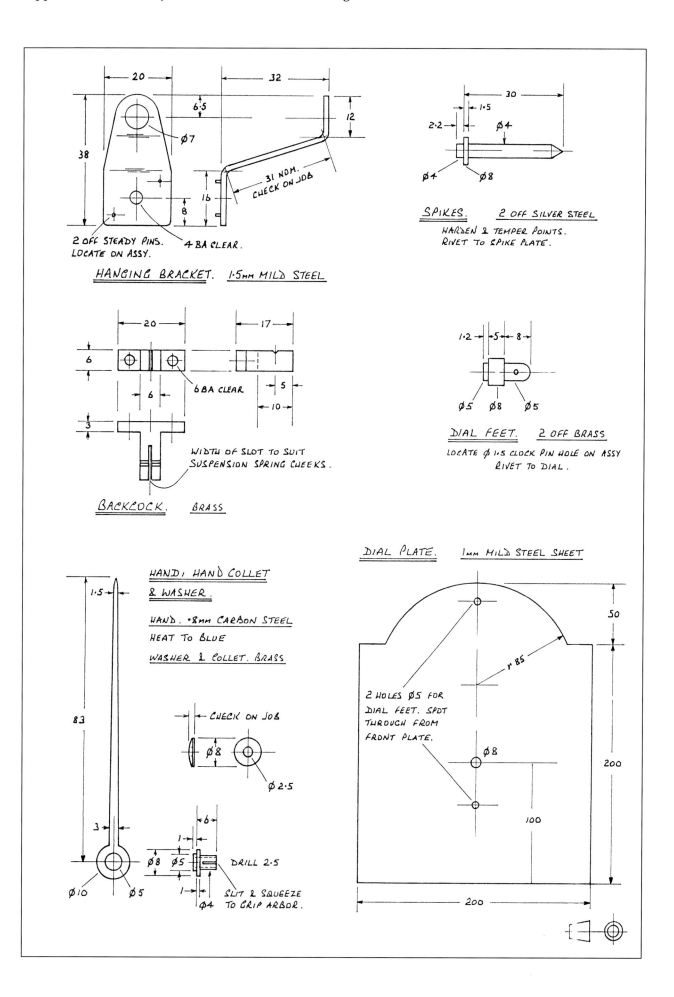

SPIKES.   2 OFF SILVER STEEL

HARDEN & TEMPER POINTS.
RIVET TO SPIKE PLATE.

2 OFF STEADY PINS.
LOCATE ON ASSY.

4 BA CLEAR.

HANGING BRACKET.   1·5mm MILD STEEL

6 BA CLEAR

WIDTH OF SLOT TO SUIT
SUSPENSION SPRING CHEEKS.

DIAL FEET.   2 OFF BRASS

LOCATE ⌀ 1·5 CLOCK PIN HOLE ON ASSY
RIVET TO DIAL.

BACKCOCK.   BRASS

DIAL PLATE.   1mm MILD STEEL SHEET

HAND, HAND COLLET
& WASHER.

HAND. ·8mm CARBON STEEL
HEAT TO BLUE

WASHER & COLLET. BRASS

CHECK ON JOB

2 HOLES ⌀5 FOR
DIAL FEET. SPOT
THROUGH FROM
FRONT PLATE.

DRILL 2·5

SLIT & SQUEEZE
TO GRIP ARBOR.

120 TEETH. MODULE ·6
O.D. 73·62
P.C.D. 72
ROOT ⌀ 70·14

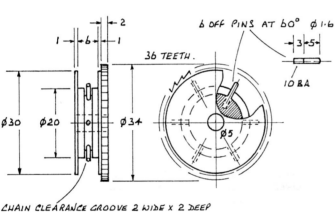

GREAT WHEEL. 2mm COMPO BRASS

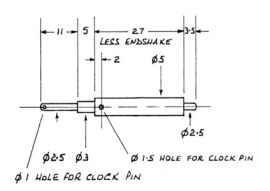

CHAIN CLEARANCE GROOVE 2 WIDE x 2 DEEP

CHAINWHEEL/RATCHET. BRASS

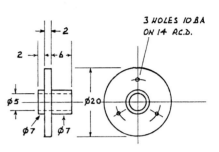

GREAT WHEEL COLLET. BRASS.

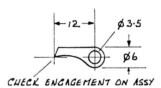

CHECK ENGAGEMENT ON ASSY

CLICK. 2mm MILD STEEL

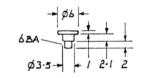

CLICK SCREW MILD STEEL

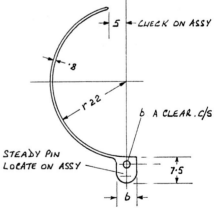

CLICKSPRING. 2mm COMPO BRASS

CUT FROM STRAIGHT PIECE &
BEND TO FIT.
HAMMER HARDEN SPRING.

ARBOR. SILVER STEEL.

"LOCTITE" GREAT WHEEL COLLET ON ASSY.

⌀1 HOLE FOR CLOCK PIN
⌀2·5 ⌀3 ⌀1·5 HOLE FOR CLOCK PIN

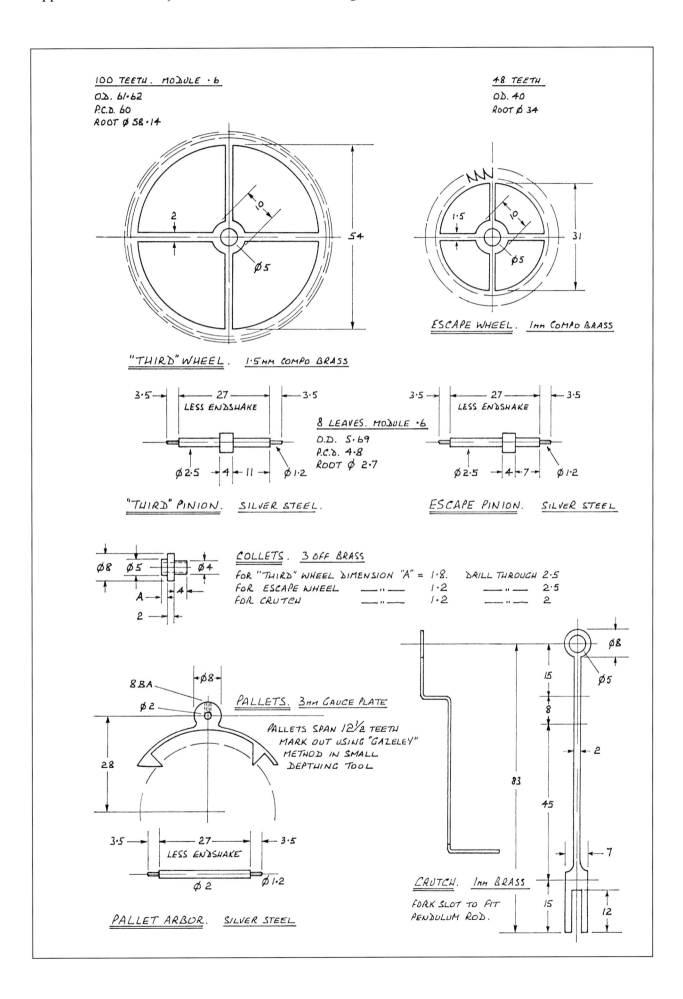

100 TEETH. MODULE ·6
O.D. 61·62
P.C.D. 60
ROOT ⌀ 58·14

48 TEETH
O.D. 40
ROOT ⌀ 34

ESCAPE WHEEL. 1mm COMPO BRASS

"THIRD" WHEEL. 1·5mm COMPO BRASS

3·5   27   3·5
LESS ENDSHAKE

8 LEAVES. MODULE ·6
O.D. 5·69
P.C.D. 4·8
ROOT ⌀ 2·7

3·5   27   3·5
LESS ENDSHAKE

⌀2·5 4 11 ⌀1·2

"THIRD" PINION. SILVER STEEL.

⌀2·5 4 7 ⌀1·2

ESCAPE PINION. SILVER STEEL

COLLETS. 3 OFF BRASS

FOR "THIRD" WHEEL DIMENSION "A" = 1·8.   DRILL THROUGH 2·5
FOR ESCAPE WHEEL   —"—   1·2   —"—   2·5
FOR CRUTCH   —"—   1·2   —"—   2

⌀8 ⌀5 ⌀4
A   4
2

8 BA
⌀2
⌀8

PALLETS. 3mm GAUGE PLATE

PALLETS SPAN 12½ TEETH
MARK OUT USING "GAZELEY"
METHOD IN SMALL
DEPTHING TOOL

28

3·5   27   3·5
LESS ENDSHAKE

⌀2   ⌀1·2

PALLET ARBOR. SILVER STEEL

⌀8
⌀5
15
8
2
83
45
7
15
12

CRUTCH. 1mm BRASS

FORK SLOT TO FIT
PENDULUM ROD.

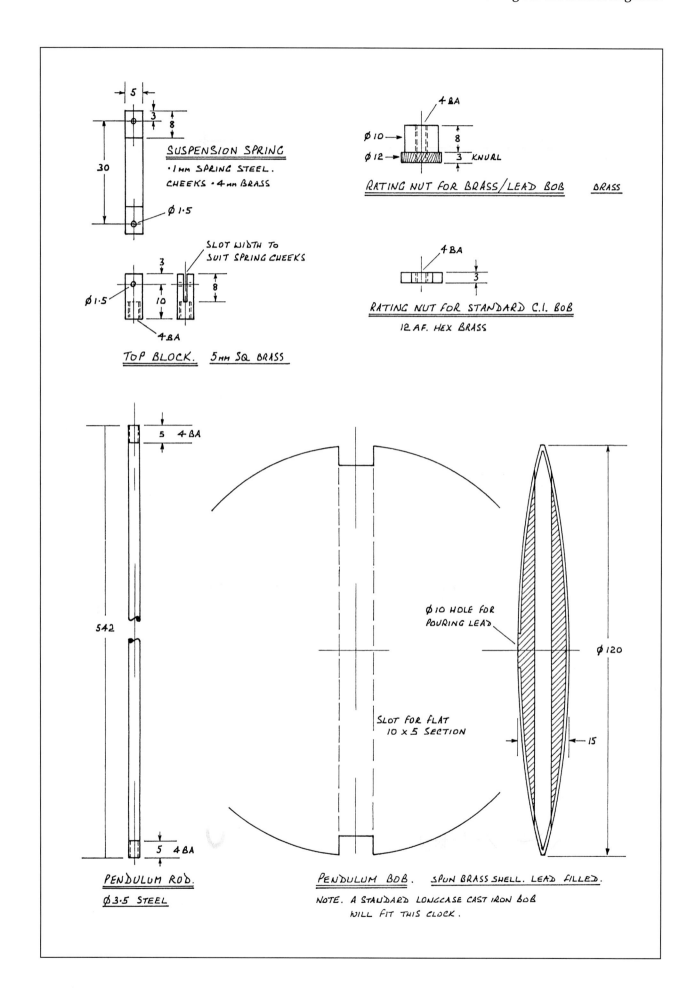

SUSPENSION SPRING
·1MM SPRING STEEL.
CHEEKS ·4mm BRASS

Ø 1·5

RATING NUT FOR BRASS/LEAD BOB   BRASS

SLOT WIDTH TO
SUIT SPRING CHEEKS

Ø1·5

4BA

TOP BLOCK.   5MM SQ BRASS

RATING NUT FOR STANDARD C.I. BOB
12 A.F. HEX BRASS

5 4BA

Ø 10 HOLE FOR
POURING LEAD

Ø 120

542

SLOT FOR FLAT
10 × 5 SECTION

15

5 4BA

PENDULUM ROD.

Ø3·5 STEEL

PENDULUM BOB.   SPUN BRASS SHELL. LEAD FILLED.

NOTE. A STANDARD LONGCASE CAST IRON BOB
WILL FIT THIS CLOCK.

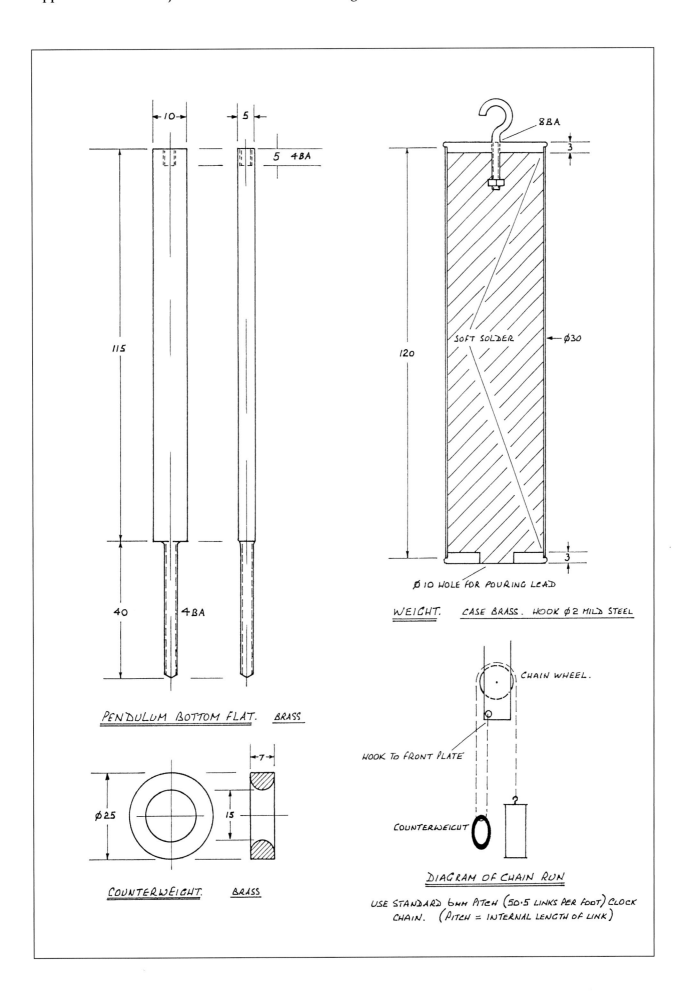

10

5

5   4BA

115

8BA

3

SOFT SOLDER   ⌀30

120

3

⌀10 HOLE FOR POURING LEAD

WEIGHT.   CASE BRASS. HOOK ⌀2 MILD STEEL

40   4BA

PENDULUM BOTTOM FLAT.   BRASS

CHAIN WHEEL.

HOOK TO FRONT PLATE

⌀25   7   15

COUNTERWEIGHT

COUNTERWEIGHT.   BRASS

DIAGRAM OF CHAIN RUN

USE STANDARD 6MM PITCH (50·5 LINKS PER FOOT) CLOCK CHAIN. (PITCH = INTERNAL LENGTH OF LINK)

Appendix V
Perforated Strip for Making Division Plates

If you have no easy access to used bandsaw blades for making division plates (see chapter on wheel-cutting), then an alternative is to use home made perforated strip.

You will need 60 - 80 cm of brass, steel or hard plastic strip or tape with a section of about 6mm x 0.5 or 1mm, although this size is obviously not critical. It needs to be accurately drilled with as many holes as required for the highest number on the proposed dividing plate. I would suggest 150 holes at about 3mm pitch. This will give you a count of 144 with 6 holes to overlap. When placed around the edge of the wooden disc a couple of tapered clock pins through the overlapping holes will hold it in place. If you need to use one of the pinned holes for indexing then the pin can be moved (or removed) for that purpose, hence the 5 or 6 hole overlap and the use of 2 pins.

The strip can be accurately drilled using the little jig illustrated. The groove must obviously be the same width as the strip you are using and two holes are drilled at the required pitch, one being fitted with a close-fitting pin.

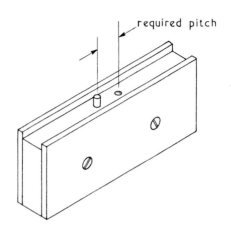

JIG FOR DRILLING PERFORATED STRIP

In use, the jig is clamped in the machine vice on the bench drilling table with the open hole directly under the drill. The first hole is drilled in the strip and that hole then placed over the pin and the second hole drilled. Then ditto repeato until you have the required number of holes. It is obviously sensible to clamp or bolt the machine vice to the drilling table to be absolutely sure that it cannot move slightly and upset the accuracy of your hole spacing.